The world through blunted sight

The world through blunted sight

An inquiry into the influence of defective vision on art and character

PATRICK TREVOR-ROPER

with 29 color plates
78 in monochrome
and 5 line drawings

THE BOBBS-MERRILL COMPANY, INC.

INDIANAPOLIS · NEW YORK

To R.M. and D.S.-T.

First American edition 1970

The Bobbs-Merrill Co., Inc.
Indianapolis · New York

© 1970 Thames and Hudson Ltd, London

Printed and bound in Great Britain.

Library of Congress Catalog Card No. 73–123237

Contents

Preface

Throughout these pages I have sought to trace the influence of altered vision on the personality of man; and, by reflecting on some writers and painters whose sight was impaired, to harness the nature of this impediment to the pattern of their artistry.

It is always rash for a scientist to venture from the solid shores of his exact science into such speculative waters; and, if I have seemed to flounder among too many unrelated disciplines, let me plead that, by constantly retreating behind the theories and experiments of others, I have tried to let these speak for themselves, and only rarely presumed myself to arbitrate. I am conscious, too, that I may have digressed more than a little on the way. Perhaps this also may be excused, for the marches of our subject are ill-defined, and there are some tantalizing pastures just off-course, into which it was a constant temptation to stray.

Introduction

Man is a visual animal. About half of the fibres that convey sensation to our brains stem from the optic nerves. We live in a world almost wholly orientated by sight, and we seek our food, sex and shelter through information provided by our retinal images.

The sense of smell, which dominated the lives of most of our vertebrate ancestors, has so shrunk in importance that it now gives us little beyond a minor aesthetic pleasure, principally when we are eating, and has a negligible sexual or survival value. (It generally fails to tell us if the food we are eating is poisonous, and only warns us when it is indigestible through decay.) The sense of hearing has never rated very high in our evolutionary ascent. It emerged in our aquatic forebears as a refinement of the organ of balance (which told them whether they were the right way up, and whether they were moving) – an organ that had again shrunk in importance by the time we became human, and our eyes had largely usurped its function. Initially our hearing helped us to find our mates; later it also became a way of signalling alarm to our fellows and occasionally of asserting our territory. But it has remained throughout evolution as a means of communication, and has little relevance in helping us to assess the external world, except second-hand from the accounts of a sighted companion.

Just as the evolution of Stone-Age man entailed a gradual dominance of vision over the other senses, our subsequent history has registered a far greater change of evolutionary direction, comparable to the emergence of organic life itself, since, in this new phase, the further layers of knowledge that each generation acquired were accumulated outside the individual, and thus formed an ever-increasing repository for his successors to inherit. This latest super-evolution of man was made possible largely by his discovery of the art of abstracting ideas and images, which could then be projected orally or visually, and crystallized as pictures or, in schematic form, as a written language.

But in our new symbol-dominated lands that lie well to the East of Eden, it is not just the wisdom of the world that accumulates: each man-made imprint left for posterity carries with it also a reflection of the personality of its individual maker. And it is from a study of some of these imprints in our literature and art that we can hazard certain deductions, beyond the information that the imprints were intended to convey. For, in telling us something of the personality of the imprinter, they may incidentally suggest how his character could have been moulded by a dulling or distortion of that visual input by which his personality was nourished, and through which its orientation was achieved.

For beneath our visual selves, beneath even the old Adam, lies buried that mammalian and pre-mammalian self, which feels and smells and intuitively or instinctively apprehends. When the dominating eyes are blunted, these 'older' senses again become the masters, and to that extent a new *persona* is born.

This, then, is the burden of the chapters that follow. The sight can be blunted in many ways; the retinal image can be distorted or blurred at certain distances, our colour values can be or go awry, our eyes can fail to work in unison, or the fields of our vision can shrink, and finally the sight can be lost entirely.

The changes in personality that follow such a dulling of our sight are subtle and complex; and any psychological assessment of them would be suspect, because it would depend so much upon the attitude and experience of the observer. But in the outward expression of the personality, as crystallized in its writing and painting, we at least have a projection that admits an objective analysis, which applies not only to the personalities within our reach, but extends back in history to the days when artistry first emerged, and the first ballads were sung.

It must be emphasized that the influence of any such physical and physiological factors on the pattern of our arts is, if present at all, almost inevitably of minor importance, and could rarely apply outside naturalistic paintings or writing. But in the un-inhibited domain of contemporary art and literature, even these smallest factors should not be overlooked.

CHAPTER ONE

The unfocused image

The great majority of those whose sight is poor have had their eyes 'blunted' because the optical proportions of their eyeballs are awry, so that they cannot receive a clearly focused image on their retinas, although the eyes are otherwise perfectly sound. Such optical anomalies can usually be neutralized by spectacles; but until the present century these were a luxury, normally chosen by trial and error from an itinerant vendor's tray, and frowned on by most nineteenth-century oculists, who held them to be damaging to the eyes.

But even if spectacles are worn, it is never quite the same as having a normal eye. Often the child has already suffered from his inadequacy before the glasses are prescribed, and he may well feel still more of an outsider when forced to wear these clumsy and fragile 'crutches'. Throughout life he knows he is different. And even those who escape the need for spectacles till the usual reading difficulties of middle age, face a potential psychological trauma with this first stigma of their gradual bodily decay.

To understand the optical basis of vision, we may consider the eyeball simply as a box-camera, spherical rather than cubical in shape, so that it can rotate easily within the orbit, but with almost identical components. Thus our adjustable pupil corresponds to the variable aperture of the camera's 'iris diaphragm', our cornea and lens (whose convexity can be augmented by contraction of the focusing muscle) correspond to the camera's convex lens (whose power can similarly be augmented for close range), and our retina corresponds to the film, both of these being placed at a fixed distance behind the lens, according to the focal length of the lens system.

But biology abhors the exact dimensions that are so integral in physics; and, just as the limbs and other bodily components vary in length and contour from the standard mean, so the eyeball is usually just a little longer or shorter than the ideal length that would permit an exact focus, or else the vertical and horizontal curvatures do not exactly match.

Those eyeballs that are slightly *shorter* than the optical ideal can compensate for this shortening by utilizing some of their internal focusing power (normally reserved for near-vision) in order to reduce the focal length of the lens system, and so allow a clear retinal image; but this leaves less reserve of focusing power for near-vision, and such eyes are thus 'long-sighted'.

With the eyeball that is *longer* than the ideal, the retinal image of a distant object is inevitably blurred, unless one compensates for this excessive length by wearing concave spectacles. Some cameras solve the problem of near-range not by adding a convex lens, but by being 'pulled-out', so that the lens system is made more distant from the film, since the nearer the object the further away from the lens its focal point lies; thus the elongated eyeball finds itself, like the pulled-out camera, in clear focus for near objects, whereas the distance is always blurred; and such long eyeballs are thus called short-sighted or near-sighted.

Short-sightedness ('myopia') and long-sightedness ('hypermetropia') are not specific failings of man; similar variations in the size of individual organs (including eyeballs) are common also in the animal world, but a poorly focused retinal image is generally of little consequence in animals who lack our sharpness of vision, and whose world is primarily apprehended by smell, touch and hearing. However it is of passing interest that, while cats and dogs are usually normal-sighted, and rats and mice long-sighted, along with the majority of wild animals, myopia occurs quite commonly in horses and cattle (about 30 per cent), and also in monkeys, where the myopia may be extreme. Some myopic mammals have indeed been happily fitted with myopic spectacles; and *The Banner* of 13 January 1888 records that a horse, suspected of myopia and found by an oculist to have a 'number 7 eye', betrayed 'sedate enjoyment' of the concave lenses fitted, and 'whinnied in a plaintive minor key' when liberated from the stable without them.

B54

Among humans the proportions of myopes and hypermetropes are surprisingly constant in nearly all the Western races, 15–20 per cent being myopic and about 50 per cent hypermetropic; but in China and Japan myopia is about four times as common (60–70 per cent). Semitic races are also prone

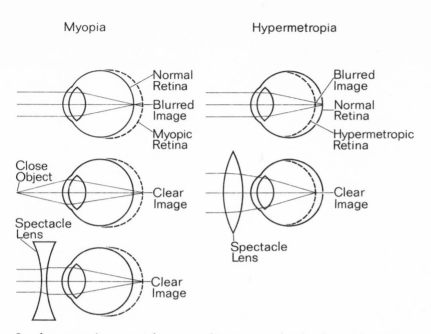

Myopia

Hypermetropia

In the myopic eye only near objects are clearly focused unless a concave lens is worn; in a hypermetropic eye even distant objects may be out of focus, unless a convex lens is worn.

to myopia, often of high degree, while this is very rarely found among Nubians. The prevalence of high myopia in Egyptians and Jews as opposed to other Caucasians, in Europeans as opposed to Eskimos and African Negroes, in Brahmins as opposed to non-Brahmins, has been attributed to their longer histories of civilization, the laws of natural selection (which would tend to weed out the less competitive high myopes in a primitive society) being relaxed in civilized groups. These refractive errors are genetically determined, and there is no truth in the folk-lore that myopia is aggravated by close work, television, or any of the other exactions of our civilized world.

An elongated eyeball, however, is not just an isolated anatomical accident in any individual. No part of us is independent of the whole in its form or function; and the myopic eye, initially but one facet of an inherited mould of the human frame, may, in a limited way, continue to influence the development of that frame, its posture and its movements, throughout life. More especially is the myopic eyeball a part of a personality structure, and its influence on the evolution of this personality may be of paramount importance. Finally, as we shall see, a reverse effect has even been contended, in which the body and its personality can themselves affect the contours and refraction of the eye.

THE MYOPIC PERSONALITY

A sixth of the population are myopic, yet the normal-sighted tend to pay scant attention to this minor physical anomaly, and even the myope has usually come to terms with his built-in impediment, with only occasional calls to remind his fellows that it is more than just a tiresome blemish. As one eye-surgeon exclaimed recently to his assembled colleagues: 'But you don't understand, we myopes are different people.'* The myopes are an important, if unvocal, minority, with a common burden which, like every other impediment, may be either stimulating or damaging to the evolution of their characters.

That myopia and hypermetropia have some influence on personality is widely accepted – the studious and rather withdrawn myope and the extroverted hypermetrope are familiar figures – but such generalizations, particularly about psycho-physical groupings, are always suspect; we must approach with caution any more exact delineation of the personality patterns. Such an influence is inevitably greater when the ocular defect develops in childhood, and it is often tempered, but never annulled, by the early provision of corrective spectacles.

Concerning the typical myope, it would be difficult to better Dr Rice's rounded picture:

B142

> A near-sighted child cannot do well on the playground because he cannot see. He will not like to hunt because he cannot see the game or the sights of his gun. He will not like to tramp because distant objects are poorly seen and, for that reason, not appreciated. He will not like races or aviation or travel or sports of any sort. As a rule these persons

* F.T.S. records one of his myopic patients whose difficulties in personal relationships yielded only after the prescription of contact-lenses (a common enough story); she explained that it took about three months after seeing clearly with her lenses before she could see clearly psychologically, and only at that point did her work start to improve.

do not like the theatre, or the motion picture, and are likely to have the idea that the latter, especially, is entertainment for children only, or, as they might say, for morons. It is because they cannot see the pictures clearly. But in school the situation is different, it is so easy to see and so wonderful to read as there are none of the diverting influences that draw the attention of the normal child, or the 'motor-minded' boy to the fields, the parks and the woods. The child who knows that he cannot excel over his fellows in games gets a big satisfaction out of the conquest of the mind that he can command. After all, he reasons, this is what is really important. Ball games, hunting and fishing are a waste of time. What does it matter if one cannot do those things? He sees the fine details. When his classmates make mistakes the book-worm jumps to his feet with his hand in the air. He pleases his teacher but he loses his friends. He gets the reputation of being a know-it-all and a grind, and is popular only the days before the final examination. He does not count in athletics or parties, he is not 'one-of-the-bunch'. Such a child as we have described is not dependent on others for entertainment and is liable to grow rather contemptuous of the abilities of others. He does not adapt himself to the surroundings and is not willing to make compromises. He is often severe in his righteousness and his rightness and may become a disagreeable personage.

In contrast, here is Dr Rice's description of the typical hypermetrope: B141

Let us consider the farsighted boy, for example. His teachers have said of him that he is lazy, a mischief-maker, dumb, inattentive, or more sympathetic teachers have said that he is 'motor-minded'. His parents insist that he is bright enough but just won't study. He plays truant; he wants to quit school and go to work; he is more interested in girls and in athletics; he is out for a good time and is nearly always a jolly good fellow. If the child is a girl she is of the tomboy type. The 'motor-minded' boy does not correct his classmates when they make a slight mistake and so they like him. He cares nothing for fine details; indeed he does not know that they exist. The game's the thing! If the umpire did not see that he cut second base then it is just too bad for the other side. He will not stand out alone and stick for a minor point of principle. He is one of the boys; hail fellow, well met, and a jolly good fellow, and why not, he is happy and comfortable, at least when he is not required to do close work indoors. He gets out in the fresh air and sunlight, he has a ravenous appetite because of his activity, he scarcely knows fatigue, except eye fatigue which he avoids. He is tanned, masculine, very aggressive and is likely to be a devil with the women.

B196

B45

There have been several attempts to assess more exactly the personality changes that accompany myopia. Studies to correlate I.Q. rating and refractive error suggest that the myope is at any rate superior in pencil-and-paper types of intelligence – probably because of his greater reading ability rather than any innate intellectual superiority. And a recent report, from a follow-up of over 5,000 children, concluded that while the short-sighted achieve greater academic success, there is no evidence that they are more intelligent than their fellows. They did better at school even before their myopia developed – which might be attributed to a home tradition of intellectuality, since their parents were probably myopic too. They were more punctual, attentive at school, had more academic hobbies and less interest in sport than their normal-sighted fellows.

There have indeed been many further analyses of the myopic personality,[1] and other observations, less fully documented, that carry conviction, as upon the sleeping-habits of myopes, who tend to stay up late, for darkness is a great equalizer, and the greater security often felt by myopic children at night-time than their normal-sighted fellows. Mystics and religious leaders, as well as musicians and artists, are said to be frequently myopic, since a blurred view of the outer world is no impediment to their inner vision: perhaps these will all become fewer, as commercial enterprise and Government subsidies commit a greater part of the population to wearing the spectacles which, in homogenizing the sight, may also shackle the spirit.

For what it is worth, we know from their preserved spectacles that the hypermetropes included Hindenburg ($+4.5$ D.) and Martin Luther ($+3.0$ D.), while Bismarck (-3.0 D.), Schopenhauer (-3.5 D.), Goethe (-6.0 D.), Schiller (-2.75 D.) and George Washington were all myopic.

It is improbable that such a genetically-determined anatomical variation could be influenced by personality, rather than vice-versa; even so, some psychologists have suggested that,

1 The earliest recorded concave (myopic) spectacles. Painting by Jan van Eyck.

2 Pope Leo X carrying his concave lens. Painting by Raphael.

3 Giuliano de' Medici, with the
prominent, downcast and half-closed eyes
common in myopia. Painting by
Botticelli.

4 Lorenzo de' Medici, of
whom it was said that
'his eyes were prominent'
and 'his sight was weak'.
Painting of the Florentine
School.

5 John Milton, who was probably myopic, although the cause of his blindness is disputed. Portrait attributed to William Faithorne.

6 Jean-Baptiste-Siméon Chardin, aged 72, wearing primitive spectacles for his presbyopia. Self-portrait, c. 1771 (Below left).

7 Samuel Johnson, a presumed myope. Portrait by Joshua Reynolds (Below right).

8 John Keats, an alleged myope. Portrait
   miniature by Joseph Severn.

9 Franz Schubert,
wearing myopic glasses.
Portrait by W. A.
Rieder.

10 James Joyce, wearing myopic glasses. Portrait by J. E. Blanche.

11 W. B. Yeats, wearing myopic glasses.

12 Our peripheral vision. An attempt to illustrate the increasing loss of detail in the images we perceive from objects that lie further away from the point of our regard, as our peripheral retina registers only a relative clarity of the essential lines and contours.

13, 14 The myopic (short-sighted) view. Near objects are in focus, but more distant objects become increasingly indistinct (left). The hypermetropic (long-sighted) view. Distant objects are in focus, but nearer objects become increasingly indistinct (right).

15 E. Gordon Craig's set for Ibsen's *The Vikings*, Act 2 (1903). The emphasis on contour at the expense of detail would seem to be in keeping with his myopia.

16 Edgar Degas, *The Bath*. His style has been attributed to myopia.

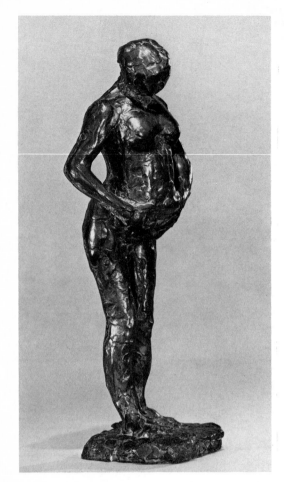

17 Edgar Degas, *Pregnant Woman*. He had increasing recourse to sculpture as his vision became less clear.

18 Auguste Rodin, *The Age of Bronze*. The sensitivity to detail in his sculpture was attributed to his myopia.

since the basic personality pattern is normally fixed in early childhood, well before the myopia has become evident, the primary change lies in the personality; and a recent theory from Japan seeks to explain just how myopia can be induced by emotional disturbances from an upset of the balance between cerebrum and hypothalamus. In fact, these last flickerings of vitalism (or first echoes of the new un-reason) can be safely ignored, and we can count it as amply established that nothing we can do – no exercises or spectacles, diet or drugs – will have any influence on the ultimate degree of near-sightedness, any more than, by taking thought, we can influence the stature that our genes have decreed.

B122

B45

That myopia is hereditary can indeed be illustrated where it has left its mark down the family-trees of many distinguished houses, with the characteristic personality and physical changes that follow in its wake; however we face the inevitable difficulty of all such historical diagnoses, for few surviving records have any bearing on a condition that was, until the present century, largely unrecognized and uncorrected.

Perhaps the best myopic pedigree available is that of the Medici family compiled by Dr Alaerts. As he tells us:

B3

> The doctor knows that every patient, especially the chronically sick, ends by creating a new personality. The myope does not escape the rule; he has an interior life different from others, a general bearing or a special personality capable of placing him in the limelight if he is gifted or energetic, or leaving him in obscurity if he is timid. With the Medicis we also find ourselves in the presence of a special mentality, a complex of infirmities, but not of inferiority, because we are dealing with gifted and especially intelligent beings. It is probably that which had the unexpected effects on their way of life, and which exerted its influence in creating the Medicean epoch.

For the Medicis also had a family history of gout (rheumatism ?), which limited their physical activities but gave rein to their intellects; when, on top of this, they inherited good taste and intelligence, all that they needed was position and fortune to ensure their success.

Since their disabilities (gout and myopia), with few exceptions, precluded successful soldiering, their enterprise found its outlet in banking, and, when they were financially secure, in scholarship and encouragement of the arts, reaching its zenith with Pope Leo X – able, artistic, corpulent, sedentary and myopic. He at least bears the only certain evidence of myopia, because of the concave spectacle-lens he was using when Raphael depicted him. (The earliest myopic glasses on record were painted by Jan van Eyck a century earlier, and one of the earliest surviving pairs of concave spectacles (of -6.5 D.) is that presented by King Gustavus Adolphus to the city of Augsburg in 1632, although it seems very unlikely that he ever wore them himself.) The evidence of myopia in the other Medicis rests primarily on the mention of bad sight, especially when they are recorded as reading well into an advanced age (none but Leo X is known to have used glasses), and secondarily on the less convincing records of the appearance of their eyes; for again and again we find mention of their 'beautiful large eyes'. The myopic eyeball is almost by definition a large eyeball, and for that reason also tends to be prominent, and usually has a large pupil; large eyes tend to be appealing, and the large pupil (as of children) may bestow the added freshness of youth.

Thus we read that the founder, Giovanni de Bicci (1360–1428), led a 'retired life', burdened by rheumatic pains, 'reading greatly in order to instruct himself up to an advanced age', and also that he had 'remarkable eyes'.

His son, Cosimo ('Pater Patriae', 1389–1464), also rheumatic, was a considerable scholar. 'In spite of an advanced age, he used to read calligraphic texts'; and his wife noted that he 'had the habit of half-closing the eyes', which he explained as 'necessary in order to see more clearly'.★

Both the sons of Cosimo inherited his poor health; and Piero (1416–69), known as 'The Gouty', who survived Cosimo, led a scholarly and retired life. A man of great taste, it was he who summoned Botticelli to paint his family. He is stated to have had 'the eyes of his family' and 'to have read up to the end of his life (53 years) without glasses'.

Lorenzo the Magnificent (1449–92) was only twenty when his father died. As Machiavelli said, 'he was the greatest protector of art and literature, more than any other prince had

---

★ This outward sign is the cause of the derivation of the word 'myopia' (μύειν ὤψ); cf. the hypermetrope (or far-sighted) who does not half-close his eyes, but tends to furrow his brow when reading.

been'; other authorities have recorded that he had 'bad sight', and that 'his sight was weak'. Although taller than average, and a lover of physical exercise, he was 'obliged to take care for his health'. He too had 'prominent eyes', although specific evidence of poor distance-sight is lacking. His brother Giuliano, who was assassinated at the age of 25, was said to have 'brilliant eyes', and it is interesting that his portraits by both Botticelli and Bronzino show downcast and half-closed eyes.

Piero, the son of Lorenzo (1471–1503), also had 'remarkably beautiful eyes', and both of his portraits (one by Botticelli) show large 'pale grey eyes with heavy eyelids'. Giovanni, the second son of Lorenzo (1476–1521), who became Pope Leo X, had notoriously poor sight, and in Raphael's painting he carries in his hand the concave lens which he is even said to have worn as a monocle while hunting. His actual lens of −12.0 D. has been preserved in the Museo di Storia della Scienza in Florence, and, if confirmation were needed, Dr Alaerts quotes from a further source that Giovanni 'read the letters always close to his nose'.

It would be labouring the issue to follow the Medici family much further, particularly among its less distinguished members, about whom relatively little has been written; but indirect evidence of short-sightedness often turns up. Thus Piero's grand-daughter, Catherine de Medici, who married Henri II of France, is described (from her portrait by Bronzino) as having 'the eyes of her race, rather large'. Towards the close of her life she wrote letters copiously, and it is unlikely that she used reading-glasses. Even the cadet branch of the family apparently did not escape this myopic taint. Thus Cosimo I (1519–74) had 'large eyes with heavy lids', and 'his pupils are too dilated for a man of forty'; and so the story continues down the line. Even the debauched face of the last of the Medicis shows the soft large eyes that had graced the features of so many of his nobler ancestors.

THE PROSE AND POETRY OF THE MYOPE
The psychology or psychopathology of the myope is indeed such a wide issue that we must be content with the foregoing rather crude generalizations, as so many other factors are necessarily involved, and so large a proportion of the population are myopic. But in the artistic expression of the individual we at least have some objective imprint of his personality that allows

27

a more exact analysis. For this reason the writings, and especially the paintings, of the myope deserve our more detailed inspection.

Many creative writers have been myopic – a considerably higher proportion than in the population at large because of the directive effects of myopia on the personality. Most striking is the influence on visual imagery, for the myope (unless he wears glasses constantly) necessarily tends to eschew detailed visual images of features that are outside his limited focal range. Thus the romantic poems of the contemporaries Keats and Shelley provide an easy contrast. Keats is often stated to have been short-sighted, and, although there are occasional descriptions (as of the Ambleside waterfalls) that seem to confound this, it could be argued that his philosophical approach – of avoiding detailed description 'so that there should be more room for the imagination' – was a rationalization of his own physical defect. Certainly his subjects are usually auditory ('Ode to a Nightingale', Sonnets 'On the Grasshopper and Cricket', 'On hearing the bagpipes', etc.), or fanciful (faeries and dream images), and when they are indeed visual, he tends to recall 'beaded bubbles winking at the brim', or 'Grecian urns', and so on, well within a limited focal range, in contrast to Shelley, who endlessly deploys his romantic imagery on distant prospects of sky and mountain. And although Keats and Shelley both use colour-images copiously (cf. p. 67), those of Keats are generally related to specific tangible objects, while Shelley's simply register the abstract hue.

Tennyson's extreme myopia is frequently recalled in the memoirs of his son Hallam, who also commented that his hearing was extraordinarily keen, and this he held to be a compensation for his short sight. 'He was so short-sighted that the moon, without a glass, seemed to him like a shield across the sky.' Although Tennyson evidently had occasional recourse to spectacles (which have been preserved), his poetic interests centred on objects that he could view at very close range, or the evocative quality of sounds, such as those that haunt the cadences of his 'In Memoriam'.*

8

B174

---

* His relative, the authoress, Tennyson Jesse, who had also inherited his myopic gene, once made this revealing comment to her oculist, when he provided her with correcting spectacles; 'Now I see as clearly as I always see in my dreams.'

Dr Johnson was almost certainly short-sighted, for he could   7
not otherwise have read in old age without spectacles, but
probably in one eye only, since his distance sight was good
enough for him to give a vivid description of the fish-catching
antics of the pelican; and indeed he loved the theatre, although
he admitted to Garrick that there were other incentives to his
theatrical visits ('I'll come no more behind your scenes, David,
for the silk stockings and white bosoms of your actresses excite
my amorous propensities'). Probably the left eye, of which
he said 'the dog was never good for much', was the short-
sighted one, perhaps the sequel to the ulcers ('phlyctenular
keratitis') he apparently suffered in infancy. If his better (right)
eye was also myopic, it is hard to know why he never wore
correcting spectacles (with which he was quite familiar), unless
it had an associated astigmatism that could not itself be corrected
at that date.

Milton, another presumptive myope, very rarely mentions   5
birds, and, when he does, as often as not it is the nocturnal song
of the nightingale, while in his rare use of colour imagery, it   B165
is usually 'tactile' in quality. He once declared that (like
Aristotle) he could see only three colours in a rainbow; which
was also noted by Goethe, whose theory of colour vision was
among the first that contained truth, and who again was very
myopic, yet refused to wear his glasses in public, and always   B71
objected to others wearing theirs.

It would be easy to add to this catalogue other myopic
poets, Alexander Pope and W. B. Yeats for instance, or Edward   11
Lear,★ whose vocabulary and imagery conform to this same
pattern, as well as a retinue who are less well-known, such as
Annette von Droste-Hülshoff, who died in 1848, and is still
perhaps the most outstanding German poetess. It was apparently a commonplace that her detailed descriptions of reachable

---

★ Edward Lear's paintings and drawings are also typical of the myope,
with the details and clarity of a miniature, before he adopted a frankly
pre-Raphaelite style. William Wordsworth's poor sight was not, as
sometimes suggested, due to myopia, but due to a lid infection by the
trachoma virus (which had reached England with the troops who
were then returning from the Middle-East war). He obtained some
relief from the traditional treatment (a copper sulphate stick), but
had many periods in which he could not read or write, and his
trouble was aggravated by an already very nervous disposition.

objects and her rare use of colour names were attributable to her extreme short-sightedness.

10   Finally – James Joyce: 'As a 6-year-old pupil in a Jesuit school, the weakness of his eyes became manifest, and glasses, that shameful curse of the small lad, were forced upon him'; and he battled on, 'with weak eyes covered by spectacles, thin bony arms and legs, almost effeminate hands and feet, highly

B68   nervous and fearful' until, nineteen years later, he had the first of a series of attacks of iritis that were ultimately to whittle away his sight. These bouts of inflammation, affecting both eyes, and soon aggravated by a painful and damaging 'secondary glaucoma', dominated his life and thoughts. He underwent ten successive operations on his eyes, after which he could still just manage to read headlines, and an eleventh was threatened

B51   before he died from a perforated duodenal ulcer.

Even before his sight was materially damaged he wrote this account of himself in the *Portrait of an Artist as a Young Man*:

> Words. Was it their colours? He allowed them to glow and fade, hue after hue: sunrise gold, the russet and green of apple orchards, azure of waves, the grey-fringed fleece of clouds. No, it was not their colours: it was the poise and balance of the period itself. Did he then love the rhythmic rise and fall of words better than their associations of legend and colour? Or was it that, being as weak of sight as he was shy of mind, he drew less pleasure from the reflection of the glowing sensible world through the prism of a language many-coloured and richly storied than from the contemplation of an inner world of individual emotions mirrored perfectly in a lucid supple periodic prose?

As time went on, he increasingly withdrew into his interior world of associations and dream sequences, and his fascination with sounds became more compelling as his sight progressively worsened. Even in *Dubliners* he had written:

> Every night as I gazed up at the window I said softly to myself the word paralysis. It had always sounded strangely in my ears, like the word gnomon in the Euclid and that word simony in the Catechism. But now it sounded to me like the name of some maleficent and sinful being.

As the associations of his words proliferated, they became enriched by his sheer pleasure in sound for its own sake, as in the frequent alliterations in *Ulysses;* and sounds, invented for their music as well as their associations, so permeated his last great work *Finnegans Wake* that the narrative is left as a faint and barely visible framework.

It must be remembered that all these inferences are simply loose conjectures, and it would be disastrous if any firm conclusions were drawn from such scattered examples of writers in whom this apparent ocular failing was one of the least components in their psychological pattern. We know that Edward Gibbon was significantly long-sighted, for his convex spectacles ($+4.37$ D.) have been preserved. Samuel Pepys was long-sighted (he probably also had a secondary 'latent squint'), and found relief only when allowed in old age to use the glasses which had been denied to him earlier as being 'unsuitable for a young man'.

B41

Among musicians myopia also appears to be common, perhaps with a similar association. Schubert and Wagner were frequently depicted wearing their myopic spectacles. Beethoven's myopic lenses (-4.0 D.) have been preserved. J. S. Bach was also moderately myopic, and it might be noted that he wrote one poem which has survived, a reflection on smoking his pipe – it was comfortably within his focal range! Gregor Mendel, the father of genetics, would also have found his labours easily contained by his limited focal range; he later had recourse to some myopic spectacles, which had then become available (-4.5 D.) and these have been preserved.

9

B154

B151

THE ART OF THE MYOPE
This simple physical deformity, of a rather long eyeball, which so affects the personality of the myope, his language and his orientation, may have an even more dramatic influence on his artistic style.

When a naturalistic painter is moderately myopic, he will probably see the canvas without difficulty, but not the more distant object he may seek to reproduce, and he is therefore reduced to painting what he sees, however blurred or distorted a percept it is. Beyond the farthest point of his natural focus, vision becomes increasingly a sort of 'peripheral vision', such as the normal-sighted person sees out of the corner of his eye, with a loss of detail and with relative clarity only in the essential lines and contours.

12, 13

B117   The following personal account by L. Mills describes graphically what the myope, and particularly the one with an added astigmatism, actually sees. The farthest point of his clear vision is only about 15 cm away; within this range, he says,

> I appreciate fine and almost microscopic detail; but beyond this, and especially at distances over 6 metres, objects become greatly blurred and colours run together with curious blends and unusual, washed-out values. There is definite oblique distortion at far distances, differing in the two eyes, and often only the essential lines of form and contour provide the clues for identification of the object under examination. Such lines frequently take the jazz mathematical shapes of cubism, and if I were a painter my conception often would be essentially geometric. At the symphony concerts my seat is in about the centre of the pit, nearly 70 feet from the stage. Three points of attention fix my interest at once: the tall form of the leader in the centre, attenuated like an El Greco drawing, two golden harps on the left flank and a strong white reflection from the curved, glistening, light-brown barrel of the bass drum, all striving for attention. The conductor holds the centre of interest, gyrating in strange contortions like some fearful wizard before a medley of mis-shapen geometric patterns in blacks, greys, whites and brown and gold; there are no details anywhere, merely blurred outlines of colour, form, light and movement. . . . The black clothes of the conductor and of the row of men next to the audience, that is, the men farthest from the strong overhead illumination, are jet-black, while the identical apparel of the rest of the musicians, directly under the lights, is grey-black, the contrast being sharp. When the harps are seen with one eye and then with the other eye, there is a prompt change in the angle of their inclination from the vertical, which represents the difference in slant given by the different degrees of astigmatism in the two eyes. The same change is noted in the size, shape and slant of the cellos and in the hands and faces. The vision of a single eye is much less distinct and brilliant than the combined vision, and distortion of objects is much more apparent with one eye than with the two eyes.

This 'peripheral' type of imagery is quite familiar to us, but usually taken for granted and rarely analyzed, while for those who are short-sighted, it is the sort of view they always have without their glasses. It is also that employed by artists who aim primarily for effects of mass, line, colour and symbolism, just as it is often used by the lazy, or the immature (as in primitive painting or child-art). This imagery was triumphantly exploited by most of the artists who came to be called Impressionists.

We can only guess to what extent Monet, who was the first   XXII, XXIII
to cultivate this peripheral type of vision, was myopic (conceivably as a sequel to his incipient cataract); but Cézanne
is recorded as being myopic, and one does not need to rely on   B117
the indirect evidence of his paintings. It is not surprising   I
that only in some of his self-portraits are his colour values and
optical proportions at all conventional. (Myopic spectacles
were by then readily available; but, when this was proposed,
Cézanne is said to have replied, 'Take those vulgar things
away.') He incidentally suffered also from diabetes, so a little   B183
retinal damage may have further disturbed what Huysmans
called his 'diseased retinas'. So was Renoir, who, according to   II, III
his biographer Vollard, when looking at pictures would step
back a few paces [in other words out of his limited near-range
of clear vision] in order to give it the effect of an Impressionistic
picture. He was then 60; and even at 64, when none of us who
are not myopic can expect to read at near range without convex
spectacles, he liked to examine petit-point close to, taking it
in his hands, and we know that he wore no glasses: he is said
to have waved them away with the remark, 'Bon Dieu, je
vois comme Bouguereau!')

Degas was highly myopic, and wore heavy lenses during   16
his adult life; as a result he was eventually reduced to painting
in pastel rather than oil as being an easier medium for his failing
sight. Later, he discovered that by using photographs of the
models or horses he sought to depict, he was able to bring these
comfortably within his limited focal range. And finally he
fell back increasingly on sculpture where at least he could be   17
sure that his sense of touch would always remain true. His
many self-portraits during early manhood show no glasses,
but these may well have been executed within his limited focal
range. He first described his loss of sight in 1871 (it was later
attributed to his travails during the siege of Paris, although he
had already been refused for the army because of poor sight).
By 1873 Degas stated that his right eye was permanently

damaged, and about 1893 some spectacles were ordered (subsequently preserved) that covered the right eye and left only a small slit on the left lens. (He was said to have had an 'iridochoroiditis' as well as his myopia, but this was probably a misdiagnosis of the degenerative changes common in myopes.)

Among these myopic Impressionists, there is also Pissarro, whose central vision was further impaired from the scars of corneal ulcers that had plagued him since he was 8 years old, as well as others to whom myopia has also been imputed: Dufy, Derain, Braque, Vlaminck, Segonzac and Matisse.[2]

15
B97
And lastly we might include Gordon Craig, who was indeed so myopic that Isadora Duncan is said to have complained angrily that he failed to recognize her across the breakfast table. His biographer, Janet Leeper, describes how he 'always loved greys and browns, very low in tone', and the other myopic legacy – the emphasis on structure and loss of detail – is even more a characteristic of his designs.[3] So it may well have been as an indirect sequel of this myopia that he lead a new approach to stage-design, and persuaded his followers of the proper supremacy of colour and form over distracting details; the sets of Reinhardt and Jacques Copeau came naturally in his wake, and this influence is widely apparent today.

B146
In sculpture the same problems confront the myope; shortsighted sculptors tend to concentrate on subjects that can be contained within their limited focal range, and to excel in the detailed observation of texture and form. In his biography of Rodin, Rilke describes how 'this myopia was destined to have the most vital influence on his art. Because of his difficulty in perceiving total effects, his instinct only rarely led him to the composition of monuments on a very large scale, in which the architectural construction is of nearly as great importance as the sculpture proper.' Rodin was accused in his lifetime of having cheated by taking casts of the subjects he was sculpt-

18
ing, since the detail in figures like 'The Age of Bronze' seemed too lifelike to have been wrought otherwise.

B128
So it would seem to be no accident that a survey of the 128 masters and pupils at the École des Beaux-Arts in Paris found 48 per cent to be myopes and 27 per cent hypermetropes, whereas in the population at large it is the hypermetropes who are about three times as numerous as the myopes. Among artists not only does myopia predominate, but such myopic artists rarely like having their myopia fully neutralized by

spectacles. Thus A. Siegrist recorded an artist who found B160
that he could only continue good painting by having his
myopic spectacles well under-corrected (an experience very
familiar to other oculists who prescribe spectacles for art-
students).

Myopia and hypermetropia have also been held to have a
direct influence on the preponderant colour that artists use.
The blue rays of light are refracted more than the red, and so
are brought to a focus slightly in front of the normal retina,
and the red rays correspondingly just behind the normal retina;
hence the myope, with his abnormally elongated eye, will see
red objects in better definition, and the hypermetrope, who
has the opposite deformity of a shortened eyeball, will have
correspondingly better discrimination with blues. This phenomenon has been capitalized for sight-testing in the 'duochrome
test'. Indeed, according to A. Patry, there is an actual shift of B128
the spectrum in a corresponding direction; thus to the hypermetrope yellow becomes tinged with green, and vice-versa
(rather crude subjective tests do appear to confirm this). Perhaps even the increasing fascination for reds in the case of
Renoir (which has been attributed to incipient cataract) was II, III
actually a result of his myopia; but it is a curious coincidence
that colours from the red end of the spectrum should play so
large a part in the paintings of Chinese and Japanese, who are
predominantly myopic (the Japanese have only recently
adopted a specific word for blue), and Patry has listed a B128
number of Swiss artists whose colours as well as their designs
could be readily attributed to their relative hypermetropia
or myopia.

Finally, both the myopia and hypermetropia of an artist
will have a direct influence on the optimum distance for
viewing his work. Artists who record on their rectangles of
canvas a relatively small view, normally use a simple geometrical perspective, the laws of which remain approximately
accurate only for such a 'narrow-angled' span. Some artists
(like Canaletto) achieve a wider-angled effect by basing their 19
geometrical perspective on two points, about 10° apart. Others
aim for a more panoramic rendering, after the manner of that
eighteenth-century affectation 'the Claude Glass' – a darkened 20
convex mirror[4] in which some (like the poet Gray) preferred
to view their landscapes, since it both mellowed the tone and
'opened them out' like a Claude painting. 21

who is known to have made
use of the Camera Obscura

However, most artists, to a greater or lesser extent, subconsciously use a 'cylindrical gnomic projection' (such as the conventional Mercator's map of the world) to transpose their view on to a two-dimensional canvas from the surface of the imaginary sphere encircling their heads, on which it seems to be disposed. But the wider the 'angle' of their view, the more necessary it is to observe the rendering from the same point as that from which it was seen by the original artist who painted it (or camera that photographed it). Even small-angled paintings have their natural distance for correct viewing – corresponding to the radius of that imaginary sphere around the head on to which the seen world is projected; and for every artist this radius is fairly constant – representing the average distance from his canvases at which he works best. This distance is generally greater for oil paintings than for watercolours, for outdoor paintings than studio paintings, in the long-armed, and, most important, in the long-sighted, and the distance is correspondingly shorter in the myope. (This optimum viewing-distance is, of course, related not to the closeness or remoteness of the subject, but only to the canvas, and in vast paintings or murals it is often very great – the artist managing to achieve this by a considerable mental effort, or by frequently stepping backwards, or by working from sketches.)

B191   On this reckoning, A. Wilson has surmised that Vermeer was short-sighted, having a short radius, although placing his subjects at a fair distance away, while Van Gogh similarly had a short radius (and therefore, one hazards, short-sightedness) but with his subjects at an unusually close range; Van Eyck had a very small radius indeed, while Frans Hals had a larger one, and is therefore a presumptive hypermetrope. Incidentally, almost as a confirmation of this, the preponderance of myopia among miniaturists has already been noted.

B22

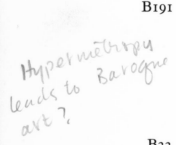

Hypermetropy leads to Baroque art?

THE ART OF THE PRESBYOPE
Hypermetropia, or long-sightedness, thus influences the colours an artist uses and his projection, just as myopia does. But the principal effect of hypermetropia is shown in the spurious hypermetropia (named 'presbyopia') due to the natural weakness of focusing that comes with middle-age and which causes a progressive difficulty with near-vision. Unless we take to glasses, reading books becomes difficult, and finally impossible, and one can no longer see the details of pictures within arm's

14

range – nor, correspondingly, fashion them.★

It is true that a fuzziness, or what art-historians would call 'breadth', is apparent in the latest paintings of most relatively long-lived artists, such as Rembrandt and Titian. Sometimes artists simply find detailed work too difficult in old age,† but this frequent change in style may well be attributed in part to a presbyopia that must have rendered the lines on their canvases increasingly ill-defined. For instance Rembrandt's portrait of Saskia, when he was aged 28, shows the usual delicacy of detail and refinement of feature, in striking contrast to his self-portrait at the age of 63, some months before he died, with the face like a rough-cast in mud. Again, in the early Titians, like *Sacred and Profane Love,* there is plenty of careful detailing, which has all gone by the time we reach a later work like *The Flaying of Marsyas.* This is not to say that such an alteration in style is primarily due to the receding near-point of the artist's clear-vision, but at least this refractive failing may bear something of the blame – or indeed the credit – for this (generally advantageous) change in style.

22

23

24

25

★ Swift's sorry decline was apparently aggravated by his unwillingness to wear the glasses necessary to compensate for his presbyopia. As Johnson wryly puts it in his *Lives of the Poets,* 'Having thus excluded conversation, and desisted from study, he had neither business nor amusement; for having by some ridiculous resolution or made vow, determined never to wear spectacles, he could make little use of books in his later years: his ideas, therefore, being neither renovated by discourse, nor increased by reading, wore gradually away, and left his mind vacant to the vexations of the hour, till at last his anger was heightened into madness.' It is tempting to add that Adolf Hitler too refused to wear glasses, and documents had to be prepared for him on the large-type 'Fuehrer's typewriter'; but the analogy cannot be stretched too far.

† As Friedlaender says, ageing artists are often forced to work in a broader way, because their hands, nerves and senses become less responsive; and indeed, this may be aggravated by structural damage in the retinas. Thus Michelangelo became nearly blind in old age (wrongly attributed to 'strain' from his exacting work). Piero della Francesca became blind 'through an attack of catarrh' at sixty. Daumier gave up drawing when he was sixty-nine. And, because of failing sight, Leonardo's later drawings became less detailed, and he relinquished his fine silver pencil in favour of a red and blue crayon, which he could see more readily.

ASTIGMATISM

As has been said, the eyeball is rarely, if ever, the exact sphere that would permit an ideally clear retinal image. Usually it is a little longer or shorter than optical perfection demands, and the bearer is a little near-sighted or long-sighted in consequence. In addition to this there is nearly always a little flattening of the sphere – usually from above downwards by the pressure of the eyelids, so that the cornea is more curved in that meridian, and vertical lines are slightly less clearly formed on the retina than horizontal lines, or vice-versa.

This condition, known as astigmatism, is thus almost universal; and the very slight imperfection of the retinal image in all but the major degrees of flattening causes little, if any, inconvenience. Indeed its existence was hardly recognized until 1825, when Sir George Airy fashioned the first correcting spectacle lens. But those who are abnormally sensitive may find quite small amounts of astigmatism uncomfortable and 'straining to the eyes', thus justifying the use of spectacles. It should be added that 'eye-strain' is much more commonly the product of an overwrought psyche than of a slightly flattened eyeball, and this often trifling imperfection is widely used as a scapegoat for some unknown or inadmissible personal travail, the spectacles serving primarily as protective screens.★ However, when the eyeball is very flattened, particularly in an oblique meridian, these higher degrees of astigmatism can materially confuse and distort the retinal image; and evidence of this can occasionally be recognized in the renderings of such astigmatic artists.

One of the standard sight-tester's methods of assessing astigmatism is to show his patient a chart bearing a fan of radiating lines; those lines that seem to him least distinct will correspond with the meridian of his least normal corneal

★ On the Continent, astigmatism has been described as the 'English disease' because of the British tendency to prescribe very weak correcting lenses, although this may be attributable to the enthusiasm of the vendor, rather than the frailty of the English psyche or an over-sensitivity of the English eye.

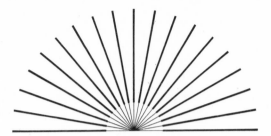 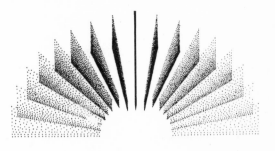

'Astigmatic fan'; sight tester's chart bearing radiating lines. As seen by an astigmatic patient, the vertical lines appearing most clear and the horizontal lines progressively less sharply defined.

curvature. The tester can then add neutralizing 'astigmatic lenses' (with their axes corresponding with this meridian) until all the radiations appear equally sharp. Thus an artist with such a degree of astigmatism, who does not wear his glasses (or, as is usual, prefers to have his astigmatic defect undercorrected), might well find, for instance, the horizontal lines to be in clearest focus, and vertical lines least sharply defined; the artist would then tend to emphasize these horizontal lines at the expense of the verticals. One of our most distinguished contemporary artists, Francis Bacon, who has 2 D of horizontal astigmatism, once described how, before the war, he used to paint without glasses; but when he subsequently examined these paintings with his correcting lenses, the vertical brush-strokes 'seemed too coarse, and broken-up, so that the images had lost all their compactness'. Another contemporary, who has a similar astigmatic defect, volunteered that he always tended to draw his vertical lines slightly obliquely, since truly vertical lines seemed to 'shimmer'; and an art student who was recently driven to use such spectacles admitted that the only other way she could get her lines clear was to smoke hashish, but that then she never had enough energy left to paint. Other such artists, especially those with an oblique axis to their astigmatism, rely on correcting the spurious tilts they unconsciously introduce, by checking their paintings in a mirror, where the distortion becomes obvious.

In fact most artists unconsciously emphasize their horizontal lines to indicate the nearness of an object, while emphasis of the vertical lines pushes the object farther away: an optical illusion that is easily demonstrated by drawing a cross and viewing it at different distances. In this way quite a small amount of astigmatism could cause a disproportionate amount of depth-distortion in the rendering.

The other form of distortion of the retinal image in an astigmatic eye is the relative elongation of those lines that lie in the least convex meridian; so that, for instance, when the eyeball is flattened from above downwards, the retinal image

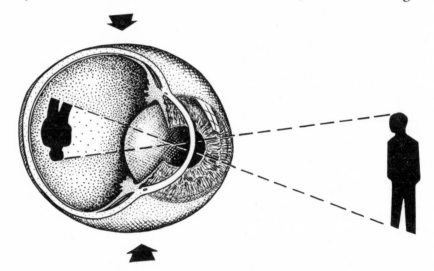

is inevitably a little broader and squatter than the subject it registers.* This relative elongation is, in fact, extremely slight (about 1 per cent in a moderate degree of astigmatism); nevertheless it forms the basis of the most familiar and time-honoured (and indeed the least probable) of all the theories propounding an organic influence on the artist's style, and thus justifies a rather detailed analysis.

* The reverse is true when such a highly astigmatic artist is actually wearing his glasses, which then cause a slight elongation of the image in the opposite direction (proportional to the distance between the cornea and its correcting spectacle-lens). And one such artist has admitted her need to amend these spurious elongations (rather than any spurious obliquity) in a mirror afterwards.

19   Canaletto, *Greenwich Hospital*. He sometimes achieved a wide-angle effect by basing his perspective on points about 10° apart.

20   A 'Claude Glass' – a darkened convex mirror, which served to mellow the tone and 'open-out' the view (Below left).

21   View in the Wye Valley by an artist using a 'Claude Glass' (Below right).

22 Rembrandt van Rijn, *Portrait of Saskia* (c. 1634). An early painting, with careful detailing.

23 Rembrandt van Rijn, self-portrait (c. 1669). A late work, with loss of detail, attributable perhaps to presbyopia.

24 Titian, *Sacred and Profane Love* (*c.* 1515). An early painting with careful detailing.

25 Titian, *The Flaying of Marsyas* (*c.* 1570). A late painting with loss of detail, attributable perhaps to presbyopia.

26–29 (Left) El Greco, *Portrait of Cardinal Nino de Guevara* (1600) and *St Peter and St Paul* (c. 1592); and (above and below) photographed by O. Ahlström through − 1·0 D. astigmatic lens at 15 axis.

30, 31   Holbein, *Henry VIII* (1539–40); and photographed by O. Ahlström through
—1·0 D. astigmatic lens at 90° axis vertical (Above).

32, 33   Holbein, *Christ in the Tomb* (1521); and photographed by O. Ahlström through
—1·0 D. astigmatic lens at 90° axis vertical (Below).

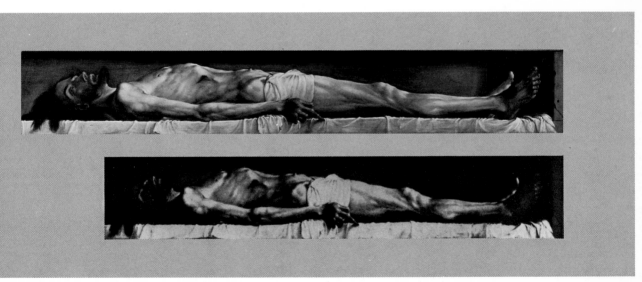

34 Lucas Cranach the Elder, *Cupid complaining to Venus*. Cranach was one of the many artists whose vertical elongations were (wrongly) attributed to astigmatism.

35 Amadeo Modigliani, *Nude with Raised Arms*. His characteristic elongations have been falsely attributed to astigmatism. But this is disproved when, as here, the elongation occurs in the horizontal axis and not only in the usual vertical one.

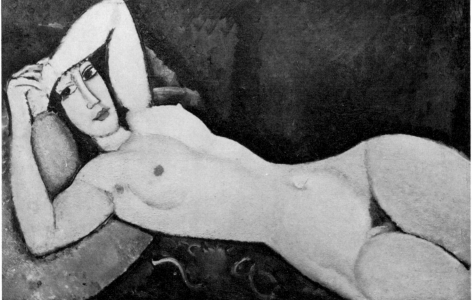

36 El Greco, *The Burial of Count Orgaz*. It was argued that El Greco's astigmatism was evidenced by the relative elongation of the angels, as opposed to the normally-proportioned foreground figures.

37 Thomas Gainsborough, *The Morning Walk*. It was even suggested that the increasing elongation of some of Gainsborough's later paintings indicated an 'acquired' astigmatism.

38 Tomb of Salvino d'Armato, 'Inventor of Spectacles, may God forgive him his sins; AD 1317'.

The classical instance of an artist whose characteristic style has been attributed to an astigmatic eye is El Greco, for in nearly all his paintings there is a vertical elongation, but on a slightly oblique axis, so that all his characters seem to be in danger of sliding off the bottom right-hand corner of the picture. It is interesting to discover how constant, both in degree and meridian, these distortions are when we neutralize them by photographing his paintings through a −1.0 D astigmatic lens along an opposite meridian (15° off the horizontal). If one looks at the portrait of the Cardinal Inquisitor Nino de Guevara (which has an incidental ophthalmological interest, in that the Cardinal is wearing a pair of archetypal spectacles, fastened with a cord behind the ears in the Chinese fashion), and then at the neutralized rendering of the same painting, one can see that the latter has indeed restored more normal proportions and removed the rather disquieting mal-equilibrium of the Cardinal, who had seemed to be slipping off his chair. The same effect is seen in El Greco's painting of Saint Peter and Saint Paul, whose figures again have the tendency to lean or 'glide' to the right, but can be stabilized by the neutralizing lens.

26

27

28

29

Less familiar are the various alleged instances of purely horizontal and vertical elongations. In the well-remembered portrait by Hans Holbein of King Henry VIII, as in many of his other portraits, the figure is broadened, presumably to make it look more portentous; the same portrait, photographed through the −1.0 D astigmatic lens, but on a vertical axis, suggests that Holbein was astigmatic with a vertically-compressed eye (as illustrated diagrammatically on p. 48). Some faint support for this theory comes when we note that in portraying his figures recumbent, as in his *Christ in the Tomb,* Holbein generally makes them long and thin, not broad and fat. And there are others, like Peter de Wint, whose long, low drawings have provoked the same diagnosis.

30

31

32, 33

Artists who tend to elongate in a purely vertical direction are common, since lissom figures are generally preferred to stumpy ones, and many of these have in their time been labelled as astigmatic, such as Lucas Cranach 'the elder' and even Botticelli and Titian, not to mention even more striking elongators like Modigliani. All these suggestions, of course, admit little serious consideration, quite apart from the basic counter-evidence that Modigliani's recumbent nudes and

B75–77

34

B22

35

B128, B24
B112, B113, B75–77

Botticelli's horizontally-stretched hands are just as elongated as the upright ones.

The 'astigmatism' of El Greco seems first to have been suggested in the Paris Medical Chronicle of 1913; thereafter came a desultory and generally sceptical discussion in the European ophthalmic journals, with the Germans generally attacking and the Spaniards protesting. Even in recent years this theory has not lacked occasional advocates.

B2, B18

The primary objection to this attribution has always been soundly based on the historical setting of El Greco's work, with his compromise between a Venetian naturalism and an underlying traditional Byzantine stylization, together with the later influence of Tintoretto. All of this is amply supported by X-ray evidence, showing that the elongations were secondarily imposed on his original sketches. But the various advocates and counter-advocates of this theory have seemed more concerned with incidental points, such as the occasional elongation of features, especially hands, when these lie horizontally (as in the portrait of Cardinal Tavera), and the more normally-shaped faces of the figures in the foreground of certain paintings

36

(such as *The Burial of Count Orgaz*). Since these foreground figures may represent the donors of the painting, it was thought that they might have required more naturalistic conceptions of themselves, to satisfy their vanity. And so it was argued that El Greco's astigmatism forced him to elongate only when he was drawing imaginary figures – without a 'sitter' to portray. Yet others contended that such elongations occurred only when the artist's astigmatism was acquired late in life,★ as opposed to the normal congenital form.

El Greco was certainly aware of devices for optical elongation, such as the convex mirror used by his fellow-mannerist Parmigianino, who had a similar tendency to vertical elongations. But by far the simplest mechanical explanation of El Greco's distortions derives from the fact that, as a right-

★ There is, in fact, a natural tendency for astigmatism to increase during later life along an axis that would promote an increasing vertical elongation. Indeed, enthusiastic supporters of this theory have counted such a natural change as responsible for the style of

37

Gainsborough's later portraits, as well as the increasing elongation of the ageing El Greco.

handed artist, he would naturally stand rather to the left of his canvas, so as to view the subject, who would be seated beyond its upper left corner; and that he did not make enough allowance for the tangential spread of its bottom right corner – which necessarily lay at a greater distance from his eye.

Quite apart from the historical and aesthetic reasons that condemn the theory that the shape of the painted image is distorted in proportion to the artist's astigmatism, there is a further natural objection – that the artist paints what he sees, and the subject will correspond to the rendering, however much they are both altered by the misshapen eye into a distorted percept within the artist's brain. In other words, if he sees a flattened or elongated world, the likeness of it that he puts onto the canvas, in order to appear equally flattened or elongated to him, will in fact be depicted with its proper dimensions.

This is essentially, but not entirely, true; for an astigmatic does sometimes, to some extent, distort along the line of his astigmatism. This is easy to confirm by making oneself see astigmatically – simply by closing one eye and wearing before the other an astigmatic lens; such an artificial astigmatic will draw an ellipse if he attempts to draw a circle 'out of his head' (that is, without having one to copy, when he will simply draw its facsimile), the circle being elongated along the line of the astigmatism; whereas if he tries to draw a line perpendicular to the edge of his paper, this will lean slightly in the opposite direction – presumably because he is making an intellectual compensation.

So it is just conceivable that for the minority of us who essentially assess our worlds haptically (by touch, contour and texture) and kinaesthetically (by the potential for action) rather than visually – in other words, making our basic assessment of objects by feel rather than by sight – there might be some such influence from our astigmatic eyes. Thus it could just be argued that the oblique astigmatic, whose retinal images are sloping, but who straightens up his percepts, since his touch and intellect tell him that the objects in fact are upright, may over-compensate when he paints them on his canvas, and the result of this could be that the picture we see is sloping in the opposite direction.

It would perhaps be proper, at this stage, to summarize the relevance of all these theories that attempt to relate the artist's style to his optical aberrations; particularly since such interpretations are always suspect, even to those who do not believe that art has any supernatural or psychoanalytic basis.

It must first be re-emphasized that such an optical distortion is, at the most, only one of many factors that can affect an artist's style, and then only when he is working in a fundamentally naturalistic framework. But, with this proviso, it would seem that the myopic painter, who paints without his glasses and avoids adventitious tricks, such as half-shutting his eyes, using photographs or guesses, and who yet strives for a naturalistic rendering, could reasonably be expected to show just those changes of form, definition and colour that have been described. The high frequency of myopes among artists, and among the Impressionists in particular, is probably not just coincidental. Clearly not all Impressionists were myopic, and there is a vast amount in Impressionism apart from the myopic changes we have noted (such as the intellectual use of complementary colours), but an artist's myopia could indeed have a limited effect on his style. In the same way the elderly (and non-bespectacled) artist would almost inevitably paint with more breadth, while the rather careless astigmatic might even shift his meridians slightly off-true. And these stylistic changes might thus have established a pattern for the individual artist, which he himself could have consciously exaggerated, or which his followers could have copied.

If we accept this, we may be tempted to wonder how different the world of art might have been if all these famous painters had been forced to wear glasses constantly. We might even agree with Mr Cross, the Vicar of Chew Magna in Somersetshire, who once declared, 'The newly invented optick glasses are immoral, since they pervert the natural sight, and make things appear in an unnatural and a false light,' or with the epitaph in S. Maria Maggiore in Florence which says: 'Here lies Salvino d'Armato, of the Armati of Florence, Inventor of spectacles: may God forgive him his sins. AD 1317.'

B71

CHAPTER TWO

The acceptance of colours

The story of the emergence of colour-vision is as curious as any in the whole evolutionary saga.

Among the invertebrates, it seems established that certain insects distinguish a variety of colours; indeed their range probably extends far beyond the limited wave-bands of our own visible spectrum, so that they can discriminate 'colour' well out into the ultra-violet – and, for all we yet know, among more distant wave-bands too. But the testing of such awareness is immensely laborious and our knowledge is very limited. Of all other invertebrates, there is so far no convincing evidence of any differing response to selected wave-bands in the whole electromagnetic spectrum,[5] apart from the crude registration of heat engendered by the infra-red waves.

But the vertebrate eye, in its earliest known form, had already established a capacity for discriminating between wave-bands from among the small range that corresponds to our own visible spectrum; and throughout the vertebrate stock, the mechanism of this discrimination (as shown by the electrical responses in the optic nerve) remains constant, even though the great majority of vertebrates can evidently make no use of it and are essentially colour-blind. Why we should have chosen this tiny span of waves – from 4,000 to 7,200 A° – out of a range that extends from the cosmic rays, through gamma- and X-rays (around 1 A°) and beyond the infra-red into the wireless waves (of around 1×10^{14} A°), and then decked this limited band with the panoply of colours as we know them, with all their social and aesthetic overtones, is one of the many conundrums with which we can look forward to plaguing St Peter when his inquisition is over and it is our turn to ask the questions.

It is true that the physical characteristics of the human eye limit the range, but eyes with tissues that were permeable or responsive to different wave-bands could well have evolved, and there is some evidence that the stickleback fish and the homing pigeon extend their colour discrimination marginally into the ultra-violet region, but to nothing like the degree found in insects. It is also true that waves farther into the infra-red would simply be absorbed by the intra-ocular fluids, but freshwater fish which have a different photo-pigment from our own can see farther into the infra-red. However, the longer the wave-length the larger the diffraction pattern; so, quite apart from chromatic aberrations, it would become impossible in principle to get sharp images. Perhaps we are not missing much on that side of the visible spectrum, as infra-red photography gives us little in the way of a new visual dimension, except in misty weather.

The evolutionary gap is so complete that we are still uncertain from which of the higher invertebrate phyla our vertebrate stock arose (probably it was from some proto-starfish): but from the 'lowest' fishes upwards, the stages are at least clearly signposted. These lowest fishes are still colour-blind, and it is only in the more sophisticated bony fishes – particularly the salmon and trout (as many anglers know to their advantage) that colour discrimination becomes established. When the vertebrate stock became terrestrial, it seems that the colour faculty, so recently won, was found to be redundant in the mud of those uncertain streams where the primordial lung-fishes had strayed, and all living amphibia again are essentially colour-blind. So too are all living reptiles with the doubtful exception of certain lizards: again one can see that colours have little relevance in the murky habitat that most of our current reptiles enjoy. Primitive mammals once more are largely nocturnal or crepuscular; and, even if their successors have often taken to the open plains, they have all, with the single exception of the higher primates, remained essentially colour-blind, so that our domestic animals, whether hunters or hunted, carnivores or herbivores, have a negligible capacity to distinguish hues from the different impulses conveyed up their optic nerve fibres.

In testing the vertebrates for colour-sense, although a great variety of species has been assessed, one is up against the same practical problems as with the invertebrates, not least in coping with the essential torpidity of fishes and the essential stupidity of birds. Birds have a special system of oil droplets in their retinas, so that they must see, as it were, through yellowish spectacles, and it may be that their blue vision is curtailed in consequence. Among mammals, a modicum of colour-discrimination may conceivably exist in squirrels, dogs and horses, but not in their fellow rodents or carnivores or ungulates (bulls being thus quite unaware of red). All lower primates (even the diurnal lemur) are totally colour-blind. The relative lack of colour in the coats of such mammals, as in amphibia and most reptiles, is complementary to the lack of useful response such colour would provoke.

Only when these vertebrates emerged from the undergrowth and took off into the air as pterodactyls or into the trees as primates did colour-vision return, and all living birds and higher primates can paint their world in colour.[6] For since their trout-like forebears had left the clear river water, they had relied for their orientation on touch and smell, which now were of little avail. At the same time, these birds and primates learned not only to see colours but to evolve the full stereoscopic vision that widens their distance and spatial judgments, and which is so valuable to ourselves and the birds, but would have been of little relevance to the majority of our earthbound ancestors.

ARTISTRY IN BIRDS AND MAMMALS

Apart from mankind, only two groups of animals seem to have discovered the joys of visual artistry, or at any rate will devote their attention to painting patterns – the Bower-birds and the anthropoid apes. These Satin Bower-birds are rare inhabitants of Australasia, and the darker male bird spends days or weeks preparing his bower for the enthralled female by painting blue everywhere, stubbing a twig till its ends feather-out into a brush, and using the juices of any blue fruits that it can collect. Blue is indeed a rare colour in nature, so the job is often tedious, and the bird is apparently grateful for any outside help – anything that he can carry he will use, providing only that it is blue – crockery, rags, blue centipedes, bluebells, bus tickets. He will even kill smaller blue birds to make off with their plumage, or snatch a tail-feather from a passing parrot. If one throws a red object, this will be solemnly taken away out of sight of the bower. All this display so dazzles

I   Cézanne *L'Estaque.*

II   Renoir *Diane Chasseresse.*

III   Renoir *The Stairway, Algiers.*
Cézanne and Renoir were evidently myopic (like many other
Impressionists) and the style of their paintings is consistent
with the distortion that might be expected from such elongated
eyeballs.

IV Van Gogh *Crows over the Cornfield*. Van Gogh's later paintings reflected the overwhelming depression of his final years.

V Goya *The Witches' Sabbath* (detail). Goya became deaf at the age of forty-seven. As the colour receded from his life, his paintings also became decolorized.

the female that it takes her mind off her primary reason for seeking out the male, and only when the rains come, heralding the seasonal swarm of insects (a diet necessary for the growth of the fledglings), does he stop. Copulation follows, and within a few days these ephemeral paints have all been washed away, and his masterpiece of decoration is gone.

B114

One cannot help wondering at this strange insistence on blue, particularly when we remember that farm of white leghorns, recorded from the Essex Penitentiary in New Jersey, which prospered only after the birds had all been provided with red cellophane spectacles, since otherwise a spot of red blood on one hen's white plumage invariably provoked the other birds to peck her to death.

B54

Artistry among the anthropoid apes is more generally familiar, and exhibitions of the masterpieces by certain ape virtuosi have been held in many countries. Some, like Betsy the chimpanzee from Baltimore, have specialized in finger-painting, while the British school under the aegis of Desmond Morris (principally Congo the chimpanzee and Alexander the orang-utan) prefer brushes. And there are many other anthropoid competitors, including a capuchin monkey from Frankfurt, and gorillas from Basel and Rotterdam. There is, incidentally, a striking contrast between the artistry of the Bower-birds and anthropoid apes. Whereas the Bower-birds paint as an elaborate prelude to copulation, in order temporarily to divert the sexual urge, the artistic activities of both Morris's chimpanzee and his orang-utan were an exercise of innocence. As soon as puberty arrived, Congo the gregarious chimpanzee started breaking his paint brushes (as if showing off before the tribe), while Alexander the solitary orang-utan simply accepted the keeper's finger together with the proffered brush, and quietly bit it to the bone.

39
B118

The choice of colour among these anthropoid artists is less easy to assess, since they generally need to have the brush loaded with paint before they will start painting; but Morris noted a definite preference for reds, in so far as they continued using the red-loaded brushes signally longer than those dipped in colours from the blue end of the spectrum. And it is tempting to think that, with the evolution of birds, colour-appreciation re-emerged near the blue end of the spectrum, while we anthropoids started re-learning our colours from the opposite spectral end – so that the red paints which Congo found most compelling may well have simply seemed more 'colourful' to him than the blue ones.

This apparent preference for red in the higher apes is again echoed in paleolithic cave-paintings, as well as in Greek and Minoan ceramics, although such a colour preference was largely determined by the relative availability of the pigments used.

The evolution of colour nomenclature in different races is another pointer to the way in which colour-awareness has reached us. In most primitive languages, the colour-names generally refer to colours in the red end of the spectrum, and one word often suffices for the whole of the blue end, from green onwards. Thus the natives of the Carolines have only one name for black, blue and green; among the Swahili, a single word, 'Nyakundu', covers brown, yellow and red, and they now have had to borrow the word 'blue', having no equivalent word of their own; while even in a tongue as sophisticated as Japanese the word 'aoi' sufficed until recently for any colour from green on through the blues and violets.

The same is largely true (as the prime-minister, Gladstone,   B66
originally noted in 1858) of classical European languages, in which there is again a striking lack of names for the green–blue range, although there is still some confusion as to the exact hue (or wave-length) that the various names designated. And this essential colourlessness of the blue end of the spectrum (typified by Homer's description of the μελαν ὕδωρ – 'black water'*), persists in Italy to this day. Thus Norman Douglas described the difficulty he had in persuading the Calabrian peasants that the Mediterranean was blue; to them and to their forefathers, it had always been black. The confused colour terminology of the Greeks, and the slavish imitation of Greek examples by the Roman poets, have left classical colours as a tantalizing jungle for the lexicographer, but of little real profit to the biologist, physicist or archaeologist.[7]

Finally there is the clinical observation that, in the recovery   B73
of sight after cerebral thrombosis, red is always the first colour to intrude – flooding the ill-defined visual scene for a period before the other colours slowly emerge.

---

* At other times, it was the 'wine-dark sea' (οἶνοψ), a colour he also applied to oxen!

If we could persuade ourselves that our spectral range, when rediscovered by the higher apes, started with red, and that they gradually learned to discriminate further and further into the blues then it would be agreeable to fancy that we humans may continue to colonize our way further down the electromagnetic spectrum, and register as colours more and more of the invisible wavebands of the ultra-violet, as yet known and enjoyed only by the insects. And, one day, we may even learn to register the wireless waves as colours, and translate sound into a galaxy of extraspectral hues.[8]

COLOUR AND TEMPERAMENT

Although the evolution of colour-vision leaves many engaging questions unanswered, it is probable that the emergence of our colour-awareness primarily reflects the establishment of an emotive response to individual colours, rather than any physiological re-orientation. And it is worth examining in more detail this relationship between colour and temperament, that can seemingly determine which of the available colours the brain will be willing to register, and how the mind may yet deploy or distort them to suit the symbolic values that these colours have acquired.

'The rôle of colour in the psychopathological deportment of man is not yet clearly defined': so concludes an analysis by L. Donnet, in a comfortable understatement. The emotive content of colours is indeed a complex issue, but of considerable relevance to all aspects of design; and there have been copious recent investigations based on studies of folklore, the aesthetic or philosophic associations in literature, naturalists' observations (such as the colour imprinting of birds), and the colour-associations in different forms of psychopathology.

B43

B155

Goethe in 1810 first suggested that the human response to colours depended largely on their *biological* cues, reckoning that red, orange and yellow were exciting or enlivening, while blue and purple produced anxious, tender and yearning responses; and indeed, such biological cues are manifestly important in many animals for provoking their aggression (the stickle-back which recognizes the red-tinted belly of an interloper) or sexual interest (the blue-behinded ape), as well as for identification of their own young and of appropriate food.

As well as providing biological cues, colour responses may be based on *aesthetic* grounds: these are necessarily vague and various, and depend not only on individual colour associations, but on combinations involving colour-contrast, complementaries and mixtures, to admit a complexity that has daunted most investigators.

Finally, colours provoke because of their *symbolic* content. Broadly speaking, these are either acquired or instinctive. Their 'acquired' significance is largely arbitrary, depending on traditions and education: thus the Devil is usually black in Western cultures, and red in the Far East; purity is signified by white in the West and saffron in the East; and a bevy of recent political and religious groups have established their own colour-labels. Certain of the 'instinctive' attributes are more fixed, such as those that depend on simple tactile influence: thus red is almost inevitably a hot colour suggesting fire and blood, and blue/mauve is cold. Others are less established – such as the green of plant-life suggesting growth and 'organic serenity', and yellow, the colour of gold, suggesting royalty (and God the Father). To which may be added a host of alleged associations that are based only on an arbiter's caprice or some metaphysical dogma.

Thus the four spectral bands – red-orange, yellow-green, blue-indigo and violet – are respectively Bilious, Nervous, Phlegmatic and Sanguine if one accepts the Hippocratic divisions; or Phosphoric, Fluoric, Carbonic and Sulphuric, for those who fancy the 'constitutions' of the homeopath. In psychometric terms the red-green bands are said to favour the introvert, and the blue-violet the extrovert.

Even apart from these antiquated systems, the relationship between personality and colour preferences fully retains its fascination for psychologists today. For instance, it has been established that we tend to remember colours as redder or greener than they really are, and this bipolar hue-shift may conceivably stem from some instinctive preference.

B166

An insight into the preferences of nursery-school children was gained by telling them respectively sad and happy stories, and asking them to draw a portrait of the girl around whom the story centred. It was then found that the 'sad' group used a brown crayon to colour her dress, and the 'happy' group used a yellow crayon, implying that colour-mood exists at a very early age. Another analysis showed that male students were consistent and uniform in their order of colour preference, while women were consistently inconsistent. As early

B92

B27

B143

IV

B23

B91
B25

as 1921 Rorschach had described the colour-relevance of the ink-blots whose value in personality assessment he had already established, assessing these in terms of impulsivity, suggestibility and emotionality. Recent research has made extensive use of the coloured blots of the Rorschach test, finger painting, and the colour-pyramid tests. Others have expanded the field by analyzing the subjects' preferences among a wide range of tartans, but the results are largely contradictory or indecisive, apart from indicating that there is a generally reduced use of colour by depressives (which one might indeed have guessed at the start).

In schizophrenia, where the whole perceptual world becomes grossly impoverished, all colours tend to die in the overwhelming bleakness of the scene. Paintings by schizophrenics betray little change in their colour symbolism, although the colour combination of black and red has repeatedly been observed in patients with suicidal tendencies, and those with acute psychosis often paint in monochrome. To this general rule, Van Gogh is in part an exception, perhaps because his depression stemmed from a different source (probably temporal lobe epilepsy). During his last summer he painted 'immense expanses of wheat beneath troubled skies', and after completing the last of these – a storm-tossed cornfield, out of which an ominous flight of crows was rising – he shot himself, clumsily but fatally, telling his would-be succourers not to try to save his life as 'the sadness will last for ever'.

Illness, fatigue and despair often tend to make the world seem, literally, less colourful – just like a deepening narcosis. Thus deafness, which causes a personality to withdraw from life and the warmth of human contact, is said to render everything down to a melancholy grey; and this is not just an emotional change, for profoundly deaf children have been found to have significantly lowered colour discrimination. A recent patient who exclaimed, 'Deafness takes all the colour out of things', spoke for a myriad of his less articulate fellow-sufferers. Goya, after an illness at forty-seven, became deaf for the remaining thirty-five years of his life,★ and all the

★ Probably from Vogt–Koyanagi syndrome and not (as often quoted) from syphilis.

gaiety and colour was lost from his paintings, as the subjects became distressing and often horrifying; Swift's writings became more and more bitter and venomous as his deafness grew ever more intense.

V

POETIC COLOUR IMAGERY
In seeking to understand the symbolic relevance of different colours, others have explored the colour-imagery of some of our major poets. Any interpretation of their findings is inevitably rendered less secure by the many factors involved; for often poets, like artists, merely have private individual preferences, and these may change with the mood of the poet as well as with advancing age. Nevertheless it is of some value to discover whether any material differences in the overall use of colour and choice of hues can be related to the idiosyncrasies or the temperamental approach of the individual poet.

In a fairly extensive survey, E. Slater found that Milton, Marlowe, Poe, Arnold, Browning and Shakespeare were all very sparing in their use of colour. Shakespeare and Marlowe indeed used less colour and more sombre colours in their dramas than in their poems. And when Chapman completed one of Marlowe's unfinished poems *(Hero and Leander),* although he retained much of Marlowe's style, colour-names kept tumbling in. On the relatively rare occasions when Milton used colour images, specifically mineral names (like gold) tended to predominate.

B162

Of the poets who used copious colour-images, Shelley and Keats were to the fore, Shelley generally using straightforward and commonplace colour-names (like yellow, blue, purple, green, etc.), whereas Keats preferred to relate his colours to other (usually tactile) images (like damask, verdurous, Tyrian, rubious, argent), a tendency still more evident with other colourists such as Francis Thompson[9] and Gerard Manley Hopkins.

Of the specific hues, most poets preferred the reds and other 'warm' colours, Thompson having a rare affection for browns, while Matthew Arnold had a penchant for whites (silver, snow, milk, moon-silvered, moon-blanched); only Edward Lear, Coleridge and Shelley seemed to favour blues and greens.

Slater concluded that the total extent to which colour is used correlates positively with the sensory or eidetic qualities of the poet's mind, and negatively with his tendency towards the abstract. Thus Browning, Milton and Shakespeare are of an intellectual stamp compared to Shelley, Keats and Thompson, who are poets of feeling. The qualitative difference (preference for reds or greens) really showed little personality or temperamental influence.

The issue is, of course, complicated by the distinction that must be made between the 'natural' colours recorded in poetry and the 'artificial' colours referring to heraldry, embroidery, jewellery or even to the four humours and other half-forgotten systems of pre-scientific eras. In the Middle Ages naturalism had barely emerged, and most of the poet's colour-images seem to emanate from a medieval tapestry. Even in the time of Shakespeare colours were still being used in a stylized way, as if in a device, and sometimes assumed not only an emblematic but almost a moral quality (e.g. *The multitudinous seas incarnadine, making the green one red*).

SYNAESTHESIA

But in the universality of art, the emotive significance of colours knows no bounds. If colours can be abstracted from their natural lights and pigments, and turned into the emblematic or symbolic labels of the poets' images, they can be further abstracted to embellish the very letters and syllables with which the words are framed. To Rimbaud each of his vowels symbolized an individual colour, and thus he immortalized them in his 'Voyelles'.[10] And indeed, such a 'colour-hearing', every sound being associated with its special colour, is no isolated phenomenon; this spilling-over from one of our senses into another (a 'synaesthesia') was first described nearly three centuries ago by an English oculist, J. T. Woolhouse, among his blind patients. It is probably commoner than we believe, because such people may have little occasion to mention these associations, which to them may seem quite normal and even pleasurable, and which, in any case, may be difficult to explain to their fellows. Colour-hearing usually starts in early childhood, along with the discovery of language; the colours tend to become brighter as the pitch ascends, and the pattern may become so elaborated that every sentence is lit by a brilliant display of coloured lights. There has been a recent report of a patient for whom all sounds, whether spoken or musical, had an attendant colouring; it is interesting that two of her vowel-colours in fact corresponded with those which

B126

68

Rimbaud had recorded, although it appears inconceivable that she had ever read 'Voyelles'.[11]

This translation of sound into colour is also familiar in classical music. Rimsky-Korsakov felt that each tone had its own specific colour (c. = white, D. = green, etc.). Arthur Bliss composed a 'Colour Symphony', labelling the four movements respectively purple, red, blue and green, based on the symbolic meanings associated with these colours in heraldry,[12] and Scriabin created his *Prometheus, a Poem of Fire,* with a 'keyboard of light' from a colour-organ, that underscored the intensity of the magic he wished to project. In fact this proved rather a failure, largely through the purely mechanical scheme whereby the light was made to 'duplicate' dully the chordal outline of the orchestral score. But the idea was soon commercialized; and 'colour-sound' and 'white-sound' devices, which projected kaleidoscopic or snowfall patterns on a screen to synchronize with musical tapes, were marketed as a social distraction, or as an 'analgesic' that found a limited use in dental surgeries and other situations where apprehension could be cloaked by such a blunderbuss sensory impact.

These synaesthesias can indeed overlap the senses in all directions. Thus it has been known (since 1669) that the partially deaf can hear better in the light than in the dark, and even spectacles have been recorded as an aid to hearing. The acuity of vision may be improved by both high and low auxiliary sound stimuli.

The 'memory-man' recently described by A. R. Luria suffered an almost total recall because of the diffusion of his synaesthesias. With every sound he experienced light, colour, and often taste and touch. The memory of a fence that he had passed on his walk was fixed because, as he explained, 'it has such a salty taste and feels so rough . . . it has such a sharp, piercing sound'.

B73
B107

THE INFLUENCE OF ENVIRONMENTAL COLOUR

I have tried to assess the intrinsic relevance of different colours in the individual, both as a passive reflection of his temperament and as actively deployed in his poetic expression. The extrinsic relevance of colours, the effect on our behaviour of the colour of our environment, is happily a far simpler issue. Indeed, the commercial incentive of interior decorators, stage designers and couturiers has given it more of an airing than it probably deserves.

It is generally accepted that the colours from the red end of the spectrum are stimulating and warm, while the blues and greens are relaxing and cool. W. E. Miles reports that in one B115 café the women employees found that they could discard their coats when the blue walls were repainted orange; and the sedative value of blue colours is used to advantage in hospitals, particularly when dealing with the emotionally disturbed. The stimulating effect of red has been shown to facilitate the muscular responses in a group of students whose reaction-time was accelerated when they were exposed to red instead of green illumination, and at the same time their estimates of the passage of time were increased as the lighting changed from blue towards red.

Yellow is a more capricious colour: certain shades can predispose to nausea, and are wisely avoided in the interiors of aircraft, or even in the food served on air or ocean voyages, while another shade of yellow has been used in decorating classrooms in order to improve the work of the schoolchildren.

The darkness of colour also gives an illusion of weight: Miles reported how workmen in a factory stopped complaining of the weight of the black boxes they were required to lift when these were repainted bright green.

Interior decorators are great individualists, but a few generalizations are permissible concerning the colours recommended in our homes. Thus it is common to provide a bluish bedroom in order to relax the spirit and lower the blood-pressure, a salmon-coloured bathroom to give the best 'rosy' glow to the exposed flesh, a peach-coloured dining-room to foster the appetite (this is said to be further enhanced if augmented by another edible colour, such as lettuce-green or apple-red); and for the drawing-room, since one's eyes are first attracted to brightness, the furniture can be displayed to the best advantage against a soft dark background hue.

Crying infants can be more readily quietened by blue light than by red, for after only fifteen days from birth some crude B73 colour-discrimination is possible. Film stars have been known to demand a background colouring to suit every mood of their exacting roles (red for romance, blue for reflection, and so on). And the choice of colouring in clothing, cars and all the other appurtenances of living is clearly a vast issue, which this is no occasion to explore.

THERAPEUTIC USE OF COLOUR

Finally, colour has been used as a therapy, not just as a tranquillizer or a psychological adjuvant, but in the firm belief of its mastery over disease. Just as John Gaddeston cured the son of Edward I by wrapping him in a scarlet coat as a specific protective against the smallpox virus, yellow has been the traditional treatment for eye-disease, since the use of disembowelled frogs by the Assyrians, and of bile by Tobias, up to the recent ocular panacea, Golden eye ointment.   B80

Green light is traditionally life-enhancing. For the ancient Egyptians this belief is said to have derived from the colour of the Nile in its July floods; the serenity we experience from country views perhaps stems from the same archetypal source. Pliny recorded that tired eyes could be restored by looking at green objects; and the emerald through which Nero used to watch his lions masticating the Christians perhaps admitted his covert need to temper that lurid scene.

Early spectacles were often sea-green in colour, being sometimes made from beryl (hence, it is believed, the German word for spectacles 'Brille'), which was thought to be both chromo-   B40
therapeutic and pharmaco-therapeutic. In those early empirical days it was not difficult to believe that the proximity of this precious stone positively improved the visual acuity, as in the   B49
use of malachite for the treatment of cataract enjoined by the Ebers Papyrus of 1500 BC.[13]

As Ten Doesschate has reminded us, colour filters provided   B40
for early civilization an acceptable compromise between the damaging effects of strong light and darkness. Xenophon had described snow-blindness, and blindness from sun-gazing was recorded by Lucretius.[14] The erroneous view that darkness   B106
could equally be damaging was even propagated by the Venerable Bede; he probably borrowed it from Isidorus, a seventh-   B12
century bishop of Hispalis in Spain, who declared in his book of *Origins*: 'nox a nocendo dicta, eo quod oculis noceat' (night was so named from the harm it did to the eyes).

The value of colour in therapy is far from obsolete today, although less blatantly or naïvely acclaimed: the coloured water in romantic flasks that embellish the traditional chemists' shops, the pink aspirin to deceive the regular white aspirin taker, and, not least, the various coloured lenses that are being ordered in over 6 per cent of the spectacles prescribed under the British National Health Service.

DREAM-COLOURS

It is sometimes argued that dreams are like old films, without sound or colour, and that colour is only supplied later, as in tinting a black-and-white picture; or else that we normally dream in colour, but the memory traces of colour are subsequently bleached out.

The relevance of colour in dreams remains a subject for conjecture. But our understanding of the process of dreaming itself has widened greatly since the recent discovery that dreaming in the adult occurs during a cyclically-recurring sleep pattern, characterized by a particular stage of brain-wave electrical activity and by rapid movements of the eyeball which are apparently associated with the nature of the hallucinative visual imagery of the dream. These rapid eye movements, noted long ago by Aeschylus, are nearly always accompanied in males by penile erection except when the dreams are compounded of anxiety (in which case the dreams also tend to be decolourized); and the movements are rare in the deeper stages of sleep, when dreaming itself is also rare.

Such dreaming occurs in about 20 per cent of adult human sleep, and has also been demonstrated in the monkey, cat, mouse and opossum (which, like the newborn baby, spends the majority of its twenty-four hours asleep). In premature babies an ill-defined sleep-state at thirty-one weeks leads to a more specific sleep at thirty-seven weeks, when the rapid eye movements can first be recorded (associated with shallow, rapid and irregular breathing, raised pulse, etc.). It is suggested that dreaming has simply been grafted on to these rapid eye movements, which are controlled by the vegetative part of the brain (rhombencephalon) and have some primitive vital function.★

Speculations on the significance of dreams abound in history; but the first reasoned appraisals followed the writings of Freud at the opening of this century, and traditional psychoanalysts

B195

B55

B87
B171
B67

★ In waking life, these rapid eye movements are also evident during 'active' thinking, when objects are imagined to be moving, and on suppression (as opposed to generation) of a wish.

still interpret every dream and its colour-range in sexual terms that may amuse or astonish the unprepared lay mind. Thus the dream-screen on which the colours are deployed is said to represent the infantile visual perception of the female breast, and the presence of the colours then indicate 'repressed anal excremental contents', on the grounds that colour-interest receives special impetus during the anal phase of development, and the colours thus expose one's repressed scotophile or exhibitionist tendencies. The specific colour is said to relate to its symbolic associations (red = blood, penis, sexual prohibitions, etc.; white = virgin, purity; green = permissiveness, youth, and so on).

B100

B63

This alleged symbolic meaning of colour in our dreams can be paralleled in its use by artists. Thus Van Gogh's use of yellow is considered to derive from the sun, and appears to be related to an ambivalence to his father, as expressed in sun-worship, while the complementary colours red and green were correlated with his bisexuality and castration anxiety.

B17

Colour in art can also establish identity – of the individual artist (like Tiepolo) who has a personal colour-style, which can serve as a signature; or it can indicate the sex, as in Egyptian art, where the male bodies were painted red and the female ones yellow. Repetitive colour dreams are said to be related to traumatic events accompanied by a visual shock in which colours were involved, or defensively incorporated on a screen; and it is considered that creative artists achieve mastery simply by re-projecting this scene in its associative colours.

Various surveys have attempted to give statistical answers to the question of degree and frequency of dream-colours. One conclusion from these is that recognition of dream colours is relatively rare, commoner in women and children, and more often mentioned spontaneously by women and by neurotics; in fact it is reckoned that, just as we rarely take note of specific colours in daily life, since we are essentially concerned with what things *mean* for us, colour is not important in our conceptual thinking in light sleep.

B116

Simpler theories exist, which might seem very naïve to psychoanalysts, but have a certain elementary appeal. For instance, some have observed that, as we are surfacing fairly slowly from a dream, we seem to traverse a colour-threshold, and these colours – usually blues and greens – may flood in to ravish us, before we finally awake, with only the memory of a vivid experience left to clutch at, before it drifts back into the underworld of our Id. So it might be argued that, since colour-vision was a very recent re-acquisition in our ascent through the mammalian evolutionary tree, it is among the first attributes to be lost as we sink more deeply into sleep, and to return only at the last moment as we re-emerge from the depths. And it then strikes us with the same vividness and freshness that it strikes the mind of the child (who, in his individual life, is recapitulating our human evolutionary ascent).

The gradient of our sleeping and awakening is difficult to adjust; but controlled sleep under narcosis affords some support for this fanciful theory – that colour-vision, as a late-comer in our evolution, is possible only in the 'lightest' of sleeps (when consciousness is not far away), and is quickly lost, along with our higher cerebral functions, as we descend to the primordial animal-self, which alone continues to function in our deepest sleep. Thus as one descends under the influence of ether from the level of the 'directed reverie' into the 'dream-like phase' – the figures of one's dream-drama may shrink in size but the colours become richer and vitalized, generally restricted to primary or secondary colours, yellows, greens and blues, but only very rarely reds (just as is true with mescaline-narcosis, and indeed with natural dreams). As these figures often seem stereotyped and segmented by heavy black lines between the coloured patches, the effect is that of a painting by Rouault, or of a stained-glass window, and the spell they may cast has a religious intensity – in the same way that the figures described by one patient as he emerged from a mescaline overdose had the postures and the compelling intensity of Old Testament prophets, with the Jehovah coming straight out of a Blake illustration. Finally, as the narcosis deepens, the colours ebb away, and a grey mist covers all.

B34

CHAPTER THREE

The withdrawal of colours

Although, in general terms, all mankind can discriminate between the full range of spectral colours, a surprisingly large minority suffer from greatly diminished colour-awareness of certain parts of this spectrum – nearly always in the red and green areas. To this 'colour-blind' world, red and green largely appear as grey, unless their colouring is very brilliant. There are numerous degrees and varieties of such colour-blindness. To some, the red and green are barely distinguishable from one another; to some it is specifically the red or the green that is apparently 'decolourized', while to a very small group the blues and yellows are primarily affected; and an even smaller group sees all colours with such diminished intensity that they live in the essentially monochrome world of their mammalian forebears.

VI

Colour-blindness is a curious sex-linked hereditary defect, affecting about one in twelve men and less than one in 200 women, almost irrespective of race or geography. Some curious variations in distribution have, however, been recorded, usually where interbreeding permits this recessive gene to become more manifest. The proportion of colour-defectives among Quakers was found to be nearly double the normal percentage (although this has been explained as the result of a breeding-out of true artists from a group 'who counted the fine arts as worldly snares, whose most conspicuous practice was to dress in drabs'). And a recent survey has shown that, if one travels down a line from Aberdeen to Plymouth, there is a progressive increase in the frequency of colour-defective males – for which no explanation is forthcoming.

B60

B180

The frequency of red-green colour-blindness does, in fact, rise in proportion to man's distance from his primitive state, with the lowest rate in the aborigines of Australia, Brazil, Fiji and North America, and the highest rate in Europe and the

75

VI   Colour-blind match. The bottom series shows the attempts of a red-green colour-blind surgeon to match the colours of the upper series.

VII   Painting by a colour-blind student.

VIII   Colour test. The normal-sighted read the figures as 74, but the red-green blind read them as 21.

IX   Whistler *Nocturne, Blue and Silver Cremorne Lights*. Whistler's 'nocturnes' have been attributed to a defective colour-discrimination.

X   Paul Henry *Dawn, Killary Bay*. Henry was proven to be partially colour-blind.

XI   Constable *The Valley Farm, Willy Lott's House*. Constable's colour values have been attributed to a partial colour-blindness.

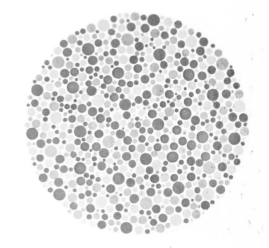

XII, XIII   Donald Purdy *Woodland Scene*. These paintings show
the typical effects of a red–green colour deficiency.

East, including the Brahmins of India. A possible explanation of this is that colour vision is less important for survival in a civilized society.

The very rare recessive gene that yields total colour-blindness is remarkably constant in frequency in different races, becoming manifest in about 1/30,000 of the population of Europe and of Japan. It becomes rather more frequent only in enclaves where consanguineous marriages are common.

B172

No specific personality changes have been established for these colour-blind minorities, but G. H. Taylor noted how criminals were readily divisible into the bright and emotional and the sombre and observant, and that the same division existed among schoolboys, with the colour-defectives all belonging to the sombre minority.

The distortion of normal colour-values is very striking, but since it is so hard to compare the colours that we see with those seen by another, one is not surprised that the very existence of colour-blindness, although surmised by the ancient Greeks, was not established until 1798, when the chemist Dalton discovered that he himself was red-green colour-blind, and labelled the condition 'Daltonism'.*

The influence of colour-blindness on industry and the professions is well-recognized today, and stringent tests are now undertaken for train-drivers, pilots, naval officers and electricians (since colour-coding of the cables is generally used). But in earlier days there must have been many problems for the colour-defective apprentices in illumination and mosaics. In 1870 Francis Galton discovered that there were 40,000 bins of mosaic stones still in the Vatican that might have shed some light on this problem; but, by 1886, when 10,752 had already been classified, his investigation had to be dropped because the

B129

price asked by the Vatican became excessive. It has, however, been noticed in recent decades that there is a high proportion of colour-defectives in the Royal Marines (perhaps as rejects from the Navy), just as there is among engravers (who were perhaps artist-rejects), although colour-blind engravers have looked on

* He bequeathed his eyes to Dalton Hall in Manchester, hoping – in the blithe mechanistic manner of his generation – that the anatomist who dissected them would discover a simple colour-filter which would explain all. Adequate preservatives were not then known, so his eyes are still waiting to be opened.

this finding as a tribute to the ease and precision with which they select the relative tone corresponding to each colour in nature.

Only occasionally in industry are the colour-defectives sufficiently high in the establishment for their distorted colour-values to become accepted. One instance is the case of 'Stroudley's Improved Engine Green', an unusual locomotive paint adopted by certain railway companies of which Stroudley was superintendent; this was in fact a golden yellow, since Stroudley was also a simple 'green-blind' and never realized the fact.

COLOUR BLINDNESS IN LITERATURE AND ART

The influence of colour-blindness on literature is little evident, since writers and poets vary greatly in their use of colour, as was noted earlier; and the colour-defective writer will simply be thought casual in his use of colour-names, when, in fact, his genes have left him little option in the matter. There is, however, one poet – Berend Jentsch – whose colour vocabulary attracted enough attention to court the label of a red-green colour defective, a diagnosis subsequently shown to be correct. An analysis of forty of his poems revealed that he used the word blue nine times, yellow seven times, green, grey, black and white three times, and red only once.

Since then, several authors have investigated the effect of colour defects on painters. D. Broschmann describes two stages   B19
through which such artists pass: the early stage, when there is a frank distortion of colour-values before outside influences have been felt, and a later stage, when the artist has learnt the various techniques of compensation, but still gets details wrong.

The effect of colour-blindness on artists was first discussed when R. Liebreich noted, at 'The London Exhibition' in 1871,   B101
how certain painters depicted roof-tops and oxen (one suspects that 1871 was rather a peak-year for such subject-matter) as red when on the well-lit side, and as green when on the dark side. This so-called 'Sign of Liebreich', that distinguished the red-green colour-blind, was confirmed by subsequent writers, and in 1908 Professor Angelucci gave an exhibition in Naples   B5
of the paintings of three such colour-defective artists. He particularly noted the fact that one artist had depicted a naked child wholly in green, since it was sitting in the shadow, and this artist had admitted that red and pale green both seemed

grey to him. Angelucci also remarked how the tree-leaves, when lit by the sun, were not yellow-green but bright yellow, and those in the shade were blue-green or sometimes entirely blue.

It seems that colour-blind painters, particularly those with a rather recessive temperament, generally try to compensate for their failing by reducing the colour-content of their pictures, which often seem a little melancholy in consequence. Whistler is an alleged example of this, and so is Carrière, who depicts his faces dimly emerging from his paintings like ghosts from the darkness. Grottger, the Polish master of pencil and charcoal, is another and well-established instance, since he conceded that colours were right out of his reach.

There is, however, a minority of colour-blind artists, generally those with a more dominant personality, who prefer to use exalted colours, but who keep clear of the ambiguous reds and greens and avoid intermediate shades, tints and hues which they would find hard to distinguish, and which in any event appear to them rather uninteresting and irrelevant. Several famous living painters and at least one art critic are known to be red-green colour-blind; while it was said by the oculist who attended Paul Henry that his red-green colour-defect was responsible for the blue mountains, white cottages and silver-white clouds of his familiar Irish landscapes. It has even been argued that Constable was partially red-green colour-blind and therefore needed to use additional red in building-up his green matches. Certainly his paintings often look autumnal – Fuseli once wrote to Wilkie, 'I like the landscape of Constable, but he always makes me call for my greatcoat and umbrella' – yet Constable himself declared in 1833: 'I never did admire the autumnal tints, even in nature ... [but] I love the exhilarating freshness of spring'. Some of Constable's pictures are indeed far from autumnal in colouring, with the blue-greens predominant and white light sparkling in the foliage; but it could still be argued that this was a natural change in the red-green colour-defective artist (because of his high 'luminosity-curve') if he was painting in a pale sunlight instead of on the usual overcast English day.

Doubtful support to this theory is also lent by Constable's own comments on the paintings of his contemporaries, which he was apt to describe as insipid or vapid, since he perhaps saw the greens as pale or fawn-coloured (conceivably because they

B128

B110

X

XI

B94

lacked the extra dose of red that he himself would have inserted). He described Farington's landscapes as 'heavy and crude' but added pertinently that they looked much better by twilight, for the natural colour-shift of vision in fading light would at least serve to darken for Constable the red pigment that Farington had used in his greens.

This theory of Constable's colour-defect is interesting, but does not take into account the attitude of artists in Constable's day to the use of colour. Corot once said that drawing comes first, then tone, and colour last; and to help distinguish brightness contrasts (= tone) he used a 'Claude glass' (p. 35) in order to exclude the colour content. Brown trees were a standard embellishment of contemporary paintings: Sir George Beaumont once said to Constable, 'A good picture, like a good fiddle, is always brown and one should always include a brown tree in every landscape.' (This so provoked Constable that he picked up a fiddle and laid it on the lawn, to demonstrate the contrast.) And if it surprises us that Constable should have told Sir George that he 'never put such a thing [as a brown tree] into a picture', we must not forget the even browner trees of his predecessors. Indeed, the majority of Constable's paintings are yet uncleaned, so that some of his apparently dark pigments are simply the result of a browning of the varnish.

A number of colour-blind artists have been investigated during recent years; and of one, Donald Purdy, who exhibited the classic failings and compensations of the red-green colour-defective, R. W. Pickford has given us this detailed report:

XII, XIII

B132

His early work was in dull colours. In the middle phase he followed the kind of colour scheme characteristic of the Barbizon painters, with a predominance of greys and browns. In the latest phase he had come to exploit brilliant colours in juxtaposition. He said that any 'transparent' colours would go together, and that he was always aiming at 'transparency' of effect. He asked whether brilliant colours were not very tiring to look at, producing nervous exhaustion, and said that he found painting with brilliant colours both exciting and fatiguing. He had developed the technique for using brilliant colours because he found that prospective buyers liked the paintings done in this way.

It was apparent that he tends to make the structural parts of his paintings in blues, browns, oranges or yellows, and that he put in reds, purples and greens incidentally. He said that he found reds the most exciting of colours, but the 'reds' which he used, and to which he referred, were usually subdued or brownish. He pointed out that in his view other people, and especially prospective buyers, do not like 'red-and-green' paintings, because they are 'Christmassy', like paintings of robins and holly. His own greatest preference is for blueish greens and brownish colours.

Mr Purdy proved to be a simple 'deuteranomalous' or partially green-blind subject; he consequently saw as yellowish all colours that were greenish to the normal-sighted, finding a 'pure green' only among the blue–green shades. Yellows tended thus to appear to him more orange and oranges as redder than to the normal person. In the same way, he called a sky-blue 'lilac', and for red he chose a purple pigment. He

B132   said he was particularly fond of 'reddish-greens' – a term Pickford had previously recorded as peculiar to the deuteranomalous.

The particular interest of this artist is that he started out tending to avoid bright colours (like Whistler, Grottger and Carrière) and then, having been reluctantly persuaded to join the dominant group, over-compensated by the introduction of bold colours, which he could poorly assess, but which he felt his public required.

B133   Pickford subsequently reported two further artists – one who was red-blind and used quiet colours, and one, partially red-blind, who used bold colours, the difference being largely

B134   conditioned by temperament. Thereafter, he collected nine colour-defective art-students who confirmed the influence of temperament. The bold ones, ignorant of their defect or insensitive about its presence, tend to use colours in a striking way that may seem original; the sensitive ones seek self-consciously to compensate or avoid its effects. He found the

B101   'Sign of Liebreich' in only nineteen out of sixty-two paintings; in a further twelve there were in fact no shadows to depict.[15]

CATARACT

An acquired colour-blindness develops during the course of a number of eye disorders, generally those which have the effect of interposing a coloured filter between the retina and the outside world. Of these the most familiar is an opacity of the lens of the eye, known as a cataract.

In most elderly people, such opacities begin to form within the lens of the eye, and rarely provoke more than a little progressive blurring of vision. In addition to an overall mistiness, the advancing cataract absorbs principally the shorter spectral wave-lengths, starting with the violet and blue; and ultimately it may permit little beyond the red rays to reach the retina. Conversely, after the cataract has been extracted by an operation, the sudden influx of these excluded blue rays, in the presence of an established adaptation to a rosy world, may abruptly change the red vision into a temporary blue vision. This colour change is mainly apparent with the rather less frequent 'nuclear' type of cataract, which tends to become yellowish or even reddish-brown; and it is generally more striking when the patient is already myopic, so that the subsequent spectacle-lens is of comparable power to that which was needed previously.★

XVIb

To most people who have their cataracts removed, the abruptness of this change is softened by the time-interval between the two operations, and the latent period that must elapse before the de-cataracted eye can resume clear sight through its new spectacles. But even artists whose professional life is so concerned with colour may not realize how blue their world has become.

XIV, XV

A colour-change towards red can be noted in the later paintings of many artists, and in a few of them it is tempting to attribute this change to the progress of a senile cataract. A ready candidate for this is Turner, whose later pictures are well known to have become more blurred and at the same time increasingly suffused with red and orange light (in Mark Twain's crude description, 'like a ginger cat having a fit in a

XVII, XVIII

★ The author Charles Singer retained as exhibits both of the yellow-brown cataracts that he held responsible for this affronting change in colour. An artist (H.S.) has recently reported that, as her cataracts advanced, she was increasingly puzzled by the pinks and reds in her garden, which seemed so much brighter than usual, and that she is now impressed by the vivid crimsons and vermilions of sunset. A Civil Servant (G.M.), recently relieved of a brown cataract, volunteered that everyone appeared to be wearing blue eye-shadow, their lips seemed rather purple, while a blueish haze covered all the buildings.

B161

bowl of tomatoes'). The medical evidence of a cataract is indeed lacking, but at least we know that Turner was not myopic, since his reading glasses (of $+3.0$ D. and $+4.0$ D.) are preserved in the print room of the Ashmolean Museum; it must be conceded that the Mr Bartlett, who tended Turner in his last years, and who styled himself 'surgeon–dentist and cupper', probably knew little (and certainly said nothing) about his eyes.

At Turner's death in 1851 the only knowledge of his medical history comes from William Kingsley's admission in a letter to Ruskin that 'The simple truth is his digestion failed through loss of teeth, and he had to have recourse to stimulants, and finally took too much.'

B101   It was Liebreich in 1872 who, in a paper to the Royal Institution, first suggested that a lens sclerosis was responsible for this changing style of artists, and cited Turner and Mulready as likely examples. In Turner's case he thought that the distortion that accompanied the blurring of detail and the overall reddening were due to the secondary astigmatism that may

XIX, XX   accompany lens sclerosis. With respect to Mulready, he noted how this change in colour value was particularly well shown in two pictures in the Victoria and Albert Museum, one painted in 1836 and one in 1857 when the artist was 72; both are of essentially the same subject, but 'if we look at the second picture through a yellow glass, the difference between the two almost entirely disappears, as the glass corrects the faults of the picture.'

There are many classical artists whose names could be added to this questionable catalogue: Guido Reni, for example, whose later pictures are mostly in reddish-brown and orange-yellow – often rather 'washed-out' and wax-like – a complete change from his youthful palette; or Renoir, if one has not already ascribed his reddish-oranges to his myopia.

But this attribution is at least plausible where there is evidence of a cataract operation. Antonio Verrio is best known in England for his spirited mural paintings during the late seventeenth century, culminating in the famous allegory of William III on the Great Staircase at Hampton Court. His earlier paintings are less familiar, but at the age of only 21 he had painted a ceiling in Naples (subsequently destroyed), and in it he apparrently included, with strange prescience, a portrait of himself as a blind man led by a dog.

He continued painting in Hampton Court, working his

way down the garden front that had just been completed, and he finished with the drawing-room of the new monarch, Queen Anne. In describing this room, Edward Croft-Murray disposes briefly of Verrio's rather maladroit conception of Queen Anne in glory (attended on the walls by her stumpy husband and an appropriately dormant cupid), which was all in a surfeit of pink colours, and concludes: 'with its riot of ill-matched colours and unprepossessing faces and figures, it hardly stands as a brilliant finale to Verrio's career. Perhaps we may excuse him in part, for his sight was beginning to fail.' Soon afterwards the self-portrait, now in the National Portrait Gallery, London, was completed (possibly by a friend), with its pathetic inscription: 'Cieco Antonio il povero Verrio.' Two years later, in 1707, he was dead. Thirteen years after this, an advertisement was published by a Dr T. Clarke, stating that, 'to her late majesty Queen Anne's great satisfaction, Signor Verrio, the famous painter, was restored to perfect sight in Hampton Court, of a blindness called gutta serena'. The evidence all suggests that this was a cataract. The fact that Verrio never recovered his sight had been conveniently forgotten over the years, thus allowing this vain boast by Mr Clarke in his advertisement.

XXI
B36

Another painter who developed a double cataract was Monet, and the characteristic changes are apparent in his latest paintings. Up till 1905 his whites and blues were still unalloyed, but soon after that the whites and even the greens became increasingly yellowish, and the blues more and more purple; in the final pictures, such as those of the water-garden at Giverny, which were done after 1920 when he had turned eighty, the form also becomes vaguer as his sight manifestly began to fail. In 1923 he submitted to a cataract operation that partially restored his sight, and then started enthusiastically retouching his paintings until all his friends and relations persuaded him to desist. Three years later he died. How interesting it would be to know, as one half suspects, whether he was 'touching out' the reds and oranges that might have insidiously been slipping in.

XXII

XXIII

Edward Ardizzone, the distinguished contemporary artist, has described the result of his cataract extraction as follows: 'Through my operated eye I see a much colder, brighter world, in which reds become pink, greens greener, and blue more intense. At first the difference was startling.' For him the main

B7

difficulty was the change in scale: 'Everything looks bigger and closer; . . . and then the hardness and brightness: in looking, for instance, at a face, one sees too much. The down on a lip, every wrinkle and pimple, and the stubble of a beard. This wealth of detail makes it difficult to sort out the wood from the trees. . . . I am rapidly getting used to the new vision and am unconsciously making all sorts of adjustments. All the same, when my second eye is operated on, I am going to miss the smaller, kinder and rather misty world I have loved so well.'

One must remember, of course, that this colour-change would not be expected except in the rarer form of cataract, which becomes brownish as well as opaque – and of course it would apply only to naturalistic painters. Sir Matthew Smith, whose cataracts were removed shortly before his death, was unaware of any alteration in colour values; the only changes he conceded were that the colours had become brighter and the details clearer.

In assessing this theory – that the artist with a reddish cataract will paint increasingly in reddish colours – the first objection that usually springs to mind is that his reddened percept should correspond equally to a normally-coloured world as to a normally-coloured canvas, so that he will surely make the canvas emerge in the same colours as the original, however falsely he imagines both to be redder than they are. This self-regulating effect normally ensures that the subject and rendering do correspond in the case of astigmatism (hence the basic improbability of the theory about El Greco's elongations), but with the red cataract the problem is rather different. Plates XIV and XV suggest that such a rectification does not always apply, and the following may be its explanation.

If one wears a brown-tinted spectacle lens, this will cut out all the blue rays, so that blue objects seem dirty grey; greens (which are intermediate between blue and yellow) become yellower, and purples (intermediate between blue and red) become redder. If one tries to paint with such spectacles, all the blue range of colours become less exactly differentiated and muddier. So the artist with a brown cataract who paints rosy scenes is rather in the position of the colour-blind who, as we noted, tend to keep clear of the colours that seem less distinct and less colourful. On the other hand, when such a cataractous painter feels compelled to use blue, he generally exalts it in order to reach through his lowered blue-perception (in this case conforming to the minority reaction among the colour-blind).

In this way, perhaps, we can account for the single patch of blue that Turner usually interpolated among the miscellany of reds, right up to the end of his life, but as an almost isolated hue in strong contrast to the seemingly endless variety of reds and oranges which he was using in the same painting.

Or else it may be that the memory-picture has become so established that the artist-patient who experiences a relative blue-vision after losing his cataract, contrasts this with that rosy memory-picture of the world which had become accepted as the true colouration. Even so, in spite of his distorted colour-sense an artist with such a cataract may well attain a more correct evaluation of the world by various secondary means. Thus he may have a long-established familiarity with his own pigments, so that, on seeing, for instance, a reddened tree, he mixes them in proportions that he knows from the past will give that very hue, even though the canvas as a result seems to him disproportionately red. (Monet apparently compensated in part for his failing colour-discrimination by having his tubes specially marked.)

It must be admitted that age itself normally shifts our colour-values so that our view becomes yellower as we pass middle age. This has been confirmed by several recent investigations[16] and can be attributed to natural increase in the yellow pigment at the central spot of the retina (the 'macula lutea'), with the result that blue is increasingly absorbed and therefore less appreciated. As a consequence of this darkening of macular pigment, which should cause a relative blue-blindness comparable to that from a brown cataract, elderly painters might unconsciously seek to compensate by stressing their blues, or else to avoid the blue colours as they become less colourful and discriminable. Indeed this change might even be said to apply to Rouault, whose obituarist observed how 'claret-reds   XXIV gave way to a profusion of yellow-greens'. After spending his life painting 'twilight', Rouault said: 'I ought to have the right now to paint dawn.'

OTHER SECONDARY COLOUR DISTORTIONS
Alterations of our colour values can be caused by many disorders other than that provoked mechanically by the reddish

filter of a senile cataract or macular pigment.★ The commonest change is a 'Xanthopsia' or yellow vision, which is a characteristic feature of poisoning by a wide miscellany of drugs, including santonin, digitalis, phenacetin, chromic and picric acids, and even snake venom; it is also occasionally noted in diabetic retinopathy.

B106 Indeed, 'seeing yellow' has been recorded since Roman times, when Lucretius, Varro and Cassius described it simply as a stigma of the mentally unsound. To Galen it was due to 'hyposphagma' (blood in the aqueous humour); subsequently the yellow staining of the coats of the eyeball in jaundice suggested that bile was the cause of this curious symptom, a view that was believed (in spite of the fact that the cornea remains uncoloured in the deepest jaundice) by speculators even as late as Goethe. But the evidence for this view is still lacking in the occasional cases of xanthopsia that turn up; probably the Romans were right after all, and the yellow colour simply

B127 reflects a psychopathic quirk. The alterations of colour-vision in psychosis and drug-induced narcosis lend support to this: a common description quoted from patients in ether abreaction was, 'Everything was yellow, bathed in glorious sunlight.'

B145 Psychopathy can indeed provoke almost any colour disturbance: one patient has been reported who had a specific inability to see red, simply because his wife had deserted him some years previously, wearing a bright red coat, and ever since he had managed to blot out this disturbing reminder of the traumatic incident.

INFLUENCE ON PAINTING OF
NATURAL EYE PIGMENT

B22 It is sometimes suggested that the warmth of colour which different painters use depends primarily on how fair or darkly pigmented they are, since in the former case, the greater amount of light that filters through the wall of the eyeball gives a colder tone to the retinal image, and vice-versa. As a

★ Indeed almost any debility can distort one's colour values. Thus William Wallace recorded, '. . . in dyspeptic states the colour vision is altered, and artists copying pictures while suffering from a bilious attack sometimes discover that, after recovery, what appeared to be a faithful copy is false and crude in colouring.'

crude generalization, Nordic painters do indeed have colder colour-tones than Latins, and the latter than the central Africans or Polynesians; and, as if in confirmation, two recently-tested albinos were both found to have defective colour-vision at the red end of the spectrum. Conversely, some people carry more yellow pigment at their macula and might therefore be expected to be relatively insensitive to the blues and violets; and to this macular pigment has been attributed the brighter, warmer centres in some of Corot's paintings, as well as the common artists' habit of heightening the blue of shadows in the periphery of outdoor scenes.

B135

B4

It should not need to be emphasized once again that all these theories which interpret the colouring that an artist uses, whether they relate to his personality, his inherited colouring or colour-blindness, or his acquired eye-disorders, can never be substantiated. Even if true, such factors are among the least important in determining the artist's style; and there are many other external influences (the availability of pigments, the instability of the green pigment used by most Renaissance artists, the environmental colouring of the artist's studio, and so on) that we have not considered. All such mechanistic interpretations are rightly suspect, but not always wholly untrue.

CHAPTER FOUR

Retinal rivalry and unbalanced eyes

As the vertebrates evolved and their eyes moved round to the front of the head, their respective fields of vision began to overlap; thus an increasing area of the outside world, lying straight ahead, was registered by both retinas. Our more primitive terrestrial forbears – amphibia, reptiles and lower mammals – remained largely nocturnal or crepuscular; in the mud or undergrowth of their common habitat, with touch and smell the dominant orientators of their lives, there was little more than a crude amalgamation of this doubled image from the central overlap of their visual fields. But when we primates and the birds became treeborne or airborne, with the wind blowing all the smells away, vision became the predominant sense; along with the development of colour-vision, we learnt to utilize this overlapping field of vision to give us accurate judgment of distances, and full stereoscopy was soon achieved.

Thus, whereas most mammals can hold their eyes straight (i.e. with their visual axes parallel) when looking at an object in front of the nose, the eyes normally act independently, with widely divergent axes. Only with the higher primates does binocular vision become so important and so well-developed that we keep our eyes straight virtually all the time, by a complicated conditioned reflex which we learn during the first years of life in the interests of single three-dimensional vision. But if illness or emotional insecurity hinders our adaptation during those difficult formative years, and particularly if we have an underlying inherited difficulty in keeping our eyes straight, they will drift out of alignment, becoming convergent or divergent, and the eyes are then said to squint. Squints can equally develop later in life after an injury to the controlling eye-muscles or their respective nerves, and the deviation can be vertical as well as horizontal; while eyes that are poor-sighted for any incidental reason will likewise have little incentive to stay straight.

A squint is commonly thought to be unsightly, but in earlier societies it has often indicated godliness and even beauty. Certain early Caribs used to force the eyes of their children to squint by severing the tendon of the rectus muscle through its overlying conjunctiva. Venus herself was frequently described as having a cast or squint,[17] although the exact meaning of the word 'paeta' is questioned.★

THE SQUINT IN ART
A squint is a common disorder; but such a deviation of the eyes should have little direct influence on an artist's style.

The most famous of all squinting painters was Guercino: 42
this was his nickname, and simply means 'the squinter'. His self-portrait makes no attempt to conceal that convergent and presumably poor-sighted eye, and his paintings may be said to have a rather two-dimensional quality in consequence.

Of more interest perhaps is Dürer, who had a divergent squint (probably inherited from his mother. His various self-portraits rather aptly illustrate the clinical sequence of this type of squint, which (unlike the commoner 'cross-eye') usually starts in older children, intermittently at first, and gradually becomes less easy to control as the years pass. In Dürer's first self-portrait, at the age of thirteen, his eyes were straight, but soon after this the right eye appears to have drifted outwards, which perhaps explains the turn of his head to the left in the Louvre self-portrait (1493), in order to minimize the deviation and its resultant double-vision. In the self-portrait

★ Unfortunately the iris, lips and hair of the statues of this period were either insecurely plugged in or only painted on, and where the plug fell out or the paint (and therewith the expression) was destroyed by weathering, even the sex became doubtful. By the time of the Roman Emperors, when the pupils were properly chiselled in, the   B54
eyes are generally found to be straight. Even so, the painting of Venus by Correggio in the National Gallery, London, has frankly divergent   41
eyes.

XIV, XV   Landscape. Two paintings of the same scene, one made before, and the other after, a bilateral cataract operation. The change in colour values (of which the patient was unaware) in this identical scene from her bedroom window, is in keeping with the natural change after the removal of a reddish cataract.

XVIa   The normal 'mature' senile cataract, appearing as a whitish opacity behind the pupil.

XVIb   The 'nuclear' type of cataract is often reddish in colour and thus acts as a reddish filter before the sight.

XVII   Turner *The Thames near Walton Bridges*.

XVIII   Turner *Landscape with Water*.

XIX   William Mulready *Brother and Sister* (detail).

XX   William Mulready *Mother teaching her Child*.
Turner and Mulready were the first major artists the changes in whose colour style were attributed to a reddish cataract.

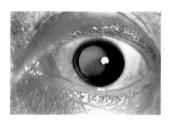

XXI Antonio Verrio, ceiling of the Queen's Drawing Room at Hampton Court. The historical evidence strongly suggests that Verrio had a cataract, and his change in colour style might reasonably be attributed to this.

46 from Erlangen of the previous year, his right hand seems appropriately to be warding off the confusing second image seen by his diverging right eye, and in that from the Lehman
45 collection in New York he might be said to be holding up his forefinger to give a point of focus for the right eye and help it
49 to stay in alignment. In the last self-portrait, it is the left eye that seems to be diverging, but this was probably because the drawing had been completed by an assistant, rather than by Dürer himself copying his own features in a mirror (or, as happens in the case of engravings, because of a reversal of the plates).

Various subjects of portraits as well as the artists themselves
51 have had their squints immortalized. Thomas Inghirami was painted by Raphael with his head turned slightly to the left and his eyes well over to the right (a compensating posture similar to that of the Dürer self-portrait in the Louvre): in his case the evident prominence of the right eye suggests that it was very short-sighted, and the squint would be a natural sequel.

This recalls the even more prominent eye of Federigo da
53 Montefeltro, whose many portraits were all done in profile to conceal the still more unsightly socket of his other eye, which had been lost in jousting. Sometimes, however, the divergence is the result of the artist's affectation, rather than his realism, when it is used to express ecstasy (if the eyes converge for near vision, it would seem natural for them to diverge when looking heavenward – beyond infinity). Indeed, it became such a habit of El Greco's saints that their eyes even diverge when down-
50 turned, as in the paintings of St Simon and St Luke. The eighteenth-century Brazilian sculptor Aleijadinho also gave a gross divergent squint to most of his figures and he often
52 supplemented this with a broadening of the nasal bridge (an occasional congenital anomaly, called 'hypertelorism'), which
B61 recalls the eye-disposition of most lower animals.

In fact most portrait-painters consciously or unconsciously give their subjects a slight degree of divergent squint to convey a rather spiritual impression, and this is evident when we contrast the relative positions of the reflected highlights on the two corneas.

An upward deviation of the eyes is also used as an artistic affectation, when the painter seeks to give dramatic emphasis to the blindness of his subject, whose eyes seem to turn

desperately upwards searching for the sun, as in the familiar
beggars of Brueghel,★ an affectation that is also adopted (for the   77
same reason) by the hysterically blind.

LATENT SQUINT

When the squint is sufficiently slight to be controlled with an
effort, the eyes will remain straight in the interest of single
vision, but this subconscious effort is a rare cause of eye-fatigue.
It must be emphasized that, when at rest (i.e. when the two
retinas no longer carry near-identical images that need to be
fused), no eyes retain exactly parallel visual axes, so that we
all have some small degree of 'latent squint'; only in the
extreme and very exceptional case does this cause trouble and
merit correction with exercises, prismatic lenses or even surgery.

Such a rare and extreme case, it seems, was Samuel Pepys,
in so far as we can deduce this from the copious complaints in
the diaries which he kept up to the age of 36. His failing sight
obliged him at that age to discontinue writing, for he believed
that, like his great contemporary Milton, he was destined to
become blind. His visual troubles have been discussed in detail
by Sir D'Arcy Power, R. R. James and others, particularly
in relation to the transient relief he gained by looking down
tubes made of black paper,† which relieved him of the problem
of binocular vision. The general conclusion is that he probably
had a marked latent convergence, aggravated by long-sightedness; and when his oculist, Mr Turlington, ultimately permitted
him to wear the strong convex glasses he needed, Pepys was
able to continue his duties and studies till he died at the age of 70.

★ Peter Brueghel the Elder is said by I. M. Torrilhon to have been
the arch-diagnostician of eye-ailments, the five beggars from his
parable of the blind representing, from left to right, ocular pemphigus
with secondary corneal opacities, photophobia possibly from an
active kerato-uveitis, phthisis bulbi and corneal leucomata.

† These were devised by a man of 60 who probably had nuclear
cataracts, and the restricted illumination would thus have allowed his
pupils to dilate enough for him to see around the lens opacities.

EYE DOMINANCE

Although about one in twenty of pre-school children squint (and one in two among mental-defectives), in adult life a true squint is rarely seen, and the eyes work in easy harmony. Nevertheless, even when both eyes have equal acuity of vision, one of them tends to have dominance over its fellow-eye, and to show this in various covert ways. Thus, if one suddenly points towards a distant object, by closing alternate eyes the pointing finger will be found to be more nearly in line with the master-eye than with its less dominant fellow.

The emergence of 'laterality' in mankind, with a dominance of one side of our bodies – usually the right eye, right hand, right foot and left cerebral hemisphere, is a fascinating issue. Even in mythology, laterality appeared as a curiosity that needed explanation. It all started, according to Aristophanes, with the creation of man, when Zeus fashioned us with faces pointing upwards and rounded bottoms beneath, in the serene equipoise of a perfect sphere, having no front or back, left or right. But men grew insolent, and Zeus split them into hemispheres, tossing the halves to Apollo, who turned their faces and genitals over on to the raw side of each hemisphere. And Zeus admonished the half-men that if they continued to be impertinent, he would split them once more, and they would have to hop along on one leg. Thus we became symmetrical.

B194

Although this myth would imply an equality between the limbs of the right and left sides, our preference for the right hand might be traced even further back, to the time when Mother Earth persuaded her Titan sons to attack their father Uranus. She armed their leader, Cronus, with a flint sickle; and when they surprised the sleeping Uranus, Cronus castrated him, grasping his father's testicles with his left hand and throwing them together with the sickle into the sea by Cape Drepanum. The left hand has been the hand of ill-omen even since. In the Muslim world, the left hand is counted as unclean, because it is traditionally used for toilet after excretion; among Christians the left hand has been deemed inferior, at any rate since the uncompromising Vision of Judgment recorded by St Matthew, with the sheep on the right hand and the goats on the left.

It seems that animals are nearly all ambidextrous, having no lateral preferences for hand or foot. It is true that (as Aristotle noted, and Sir Thomas Browne quoted) the lobster and the crab prefer to use their right claw; and 80 per cent of rats prefer to use their right paw (a preference that can be annulled by drugs, such as acetyl-choline, or removal of part of the motor area of the opposite side of the brain). There is also evidently a slight preference for the left paw in cats. But apes and Stone-Age man show no lateral preference (evidence of laterality from Stone-Age paintings and flints is questionable, although it is found in some present-day 'Stone-Age' tribes). Right-hand dominance is first established in the Bronze Age, where it seems that the sickles are generally designed to be wielded by a right hand.   B9

Nowadays dominance of the left hand occurs in about 5 to 10 per cent of the population (estimates vary from 1 to 20 per cent), being almost twice as common in boys, and about twice as common again in imbeciles. Famous 'sinistrals' include the Prophet Ehud (who turned his anomaly to such advantage), Jack the Ripper, Charlie Chaplin, George VI, Lewis Carroll, Paul McCartney and, among artists, Leonardo da Vinci, Holbein, Dürer and Landseer. Among Eastern races, left-hand dominance is probably more common among Semites and Hindus (there are no purely left-handed races), although statistics are scanty; and there has been an apparent increase recently among Western races, who no longer force their sinistral children to use their right hand for writing, etc., as do the more traditional (and particularly Islamic) parents in the East.

Dominance of the right foot is generally associated with dominance of the right hand, and occurs in about the same proportion of the population. We normally step out with our right foot (as is said to be true of horses), in spite of the conventional drill instructions; and freemasons have used a left-foot launching as one of their cabalistic signs, just as the Boy Scouts have adopted the left handshake.

An associated dominance of the right eye was first noted in 1883 by Lombroso. This probably underlies the hand and leg dominance, since the eye controls the hand; and then all three were found to be related to a dominance of the opposite (left) side of the cerebrum, which, because of a crossing of the nerve fibres at the base of the brain, controls the right side of the body. There is, however, never a complete separation of left and right, and many intervening grades of ambidexterity exist.   B9

This laterality of the brain is in fact probably the initiating factor in hand, leg and eye dominance, and is itself genetically induced (generally as a recessive trait), so we must relinquish the whimsical explanations formerly offered (e.g. by Plato and Sir Thomas Browne). Perhaps we should also reject the various speculations in more recent times by psychologists, who relate laterality to the symbolic meaning of right and left, having deduced, from analysis of schizophrenia, myth and semantics, that the right (being stronger) is the more masculine. The more one identifies the right with one's own sex, and vice-versa, the more is one's own sex seen as superior – a hypothesis that has evidently been supported by tests in which paired pictures of men and women were presented for guesses as to which was the more dominant.★

A further sequel to this hemi-cerebral dominance is the dominance of the field of vision that corresponds to the dominant eye, and therewith a greater ease in directional scanning towards that field. In other words, right-eye dominants find the right-hand side of the page easier to register, and their eyes sweep more easily towards that side than away from it.[18]

The movements of our eyes in the horizontal plane are 'easier' than those in a vertical plane. This relates to our evolutionary past when our body axis lay parallel to the plane of progression, and the muscles of each side worked in unison with each other and in harmony with their fellows. (The lateralities did not really emerge until we became erect, and the harmony, particularly of hand and eyes, was broken.) Since our gaze is thus naturally directed (in 'dextrals') into our right field of vision, our visual attention is indeed keenest in this

B193   ★ D. W. Winnicott recounts a case of a headmistress whose divergent squint registered her split personality. Her left eye corresponded to her English-speaking father, an efficient, ordered personality, while her right eye registered her disorganized and religious, French-speaking mother. On her pro-paternal, well-organized days, she used her left hand and left eye, but retreated to her right hand and eye when she withdrew to the emotional world she shared with her volatile mother.

With the full-blooded psychoanalytic approach, Winnicott counted a convergent squint simply as a reminder of the infant's early need and desire to focus on his mother's breast.

right visual field. Our natural tendency is to write from left to right, while sinistrals tend to mirror-write from right to left.[19]

There is some slight evidence from their carvings that left-handedness existed among the ancient Egyptians; and their hieroglyphic inscriptions may run in any direction, even vertically (as in Japan and China today). The Phoenicians, from whom the Greeks borrowed their alphabet, wrote from right to left, as did their Semitic successors, and the Greeks often had to reverse the orientation of their characters in order to bring them into line with their left-right script (initially they had a period of writing each line in alternate directions, a 'Boustrophedon' – after the pattern of ox-ploughing). By the fourth century BC, however, both Greek and Roman writing was uniformly 'dextrad'.

EYE DOMINANCE IN ART

In Western countries, when our right eye is the master, and we read from left to right, our eyes are conditioned to sweep over to the right field whenever they strike the left side of the page (or canvas), and the gaze comes to rest on the right edge before undertaking another horizontal journey. Thus, according to one theory, if we wish to convey a feeling of tension or movement (as in most baroque paintings), we place our principal subject to the left-hand side of the canvas; but if we place it to the right, the picture becomes calmer and more static. In Eastern races, who often write in the contrary direction, and in whom the left eye is more often the dominant one, there is a corresponding tendency to place the main subject-matter well over to the left (their pictures rarely seek any mood but serenity and calm). Indeed, P. Weinstein independently observed that in Far Eastern paintings which are bisected obliquely from bottom-left to top-right corners the primary subject-matter is generally crowded into the lower left triangle, since gravity too plays a role, while the reverse is often true of Western art.

B77

54, 55

B188

This is an engaging theory, but it must be conceded that the principal arbiter of the left-right judgment of paintings is more often just a question of familiarity. Twenty students were recently tried out on a series of paintings of various styles in alternate orientation, and nearly all chose as correct whichever orientation had been first shown to them and was therefore the more familiar. Their agreement with the artist's intent appeared to be pure chance.★ It would have been interesting to cinéphotograph such an observer's eyes as he approached the painting, to see if the gaze did not sweep from its left to right (at least in Western eyes), but this apparently has yet to be done.

There is one further point about eye-dominance in painting. Artists are usually right-handed, and until the last century had to paint in daylight. They therefore arranged the window on their left-hand side, with the model somewhat to the left of the painter, nearer the window, which thus illuminated the right side of the face. The model's right eye (the usual master-eye) looks directly at the artist, and the left eye is allowed the licence of a little divergence. (Sometimes, as in Bronzino's *Portrait of a Young Man,* this licence is stretched to the limit.) This causes a curious contrast when the artist paints a self-portrait which, rendered through a mirror, causes the left eye to appear the master eye (and usually the right side of the face to be illuminated).

B102

ANISEIKONIA

Very occasionally a rivalry between the retinas is brought out into the open, not as the sequel to a squint which frustrates their attempts to work in unison, nor by an uneasy dominance of the left cerebrum, but by a dissimilarity between the two retinal images, which cannot then readily be fused.

Such an 'aniseikonia' is almost inevitable when the two eyes have markedly different refractive errors; but this seldom matters, since one image is usually so much less clearly defined that it can be ignored whenever the discrepancy is great enough to confuse or blur the combined image. A. Linksz, however, recently described an interesting experiment by an artist, Walter Humphrey, who, by wearing an aniseikonic lens, found that his paintings took on a distortion in the manner of El Greco and Cézanne, the faces becoming asymmetric and the contours drawn towards that side where the images were magnified. One must resist the temptation to impute this curious ocular

B102

★ In another investigation, fifty New York students were shown photographs, some of which had been reversed in the printing; 75 per cent guessed the correct orientation, but the reverse orientation was selected by those who were natural Hebrew readers.

39   The orang–utan 'Alexander' at work on his canvas.

40   The gorilla 'Sophie' drawing.

42 'Il Guercino' (the artist Giovanni Francesco Barbieri), painted by Benedetto Gennari, showing the gross convergent squint that provoked this nickname.

43 Bronzino, *Portrait of a Young Man*. The model's right eye looks directly at the artist, and the left is allowed a little divergence – as is occasionally found in portraits by right-handed artists (Below).

← 41 Correggio, *Mercury instructing Cupid before Venus*. Venus is portrayed with a divergent squint, to which there were frequent references in the classics (Opposite page).

44 Albrecht Dürer, self-portrait aged 13 (1484). The eyes are still straight (Left).

45 Dürer, self-portrait aged 22 (1493). The finger may have been held up in order to steady the right eye, which is tending to diverge (Below left).

46 Dürer self-portrait aged 21 (c. 1492). The right hand would seem to be warding off the confusing false image from his divergent right eye (Below right).

48   Dürer, portrait of his mother. Her
divergent squint was presumably passed on
to her son (Right).

47   Dürer, self-portrait aged 22 (1493).
His head is turned to the left, conceivably to
compensate for the divergence of the right
eye (Below left).

49   Dürer, self-portrait as a sick man
(c. 1510). It is the left eye that now appears
to be diverging, perhaps because the earlier
self-portraits were done through mirrors and
this was largely done by his apprentices

50 El Greco, St Luke. Divergence of the eyes as affectation of other-worldliness.

51 Thomas Inghirami, showing a divergent squint. Painting by Raphael.

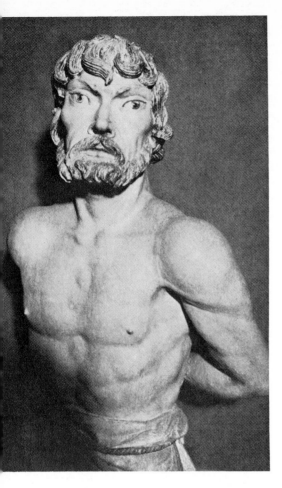

52   Aleijadinho, *The Bad Thief* (detail of
Crucifixion at Congonhas do Campo,
Brazil), begun 1796. His portrayals frequently
had widely divergent eyes, emphasized by a
broadening of the nasal bridge.

53   Federigo da Montefeltro.
Painting by Piero della Francesca.
Federigo's portraits were all done
in profile to conceal the absent
right eye.

54, 55 Velazquez, *Jacob receiving the bloodstained coat of Joseph*; and the left–right reversal of the same painting. To eyes that normally read from left to right the picture may seem less static in reversal.

anomaly to either of these masters, even when, as in the case of El Greco, the stretching of the contours is in a fairly constant direction.

Finally there are those who have different colour evaluations with each eye, not just as the natural (if usually unappreciated) sequel to a relative long- or short-sightedness on one side, but between otherwise identical eyes. Thus several artists find that they can see warm rosy tones with one eye, and cold blueish ones with the other; so they use one eye or the other, or both, according to the particular colour-value they are seeking. And in a recent press comment, an East Anglian art-teacher affirmed that she 'sees independently with each eye, so that her eyes break down tones into pure colours.' The bizarre accomplishment admits no easy explanation.

B48

CHAPTER FIVE

Encroachments on the field of vision

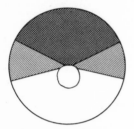

Human

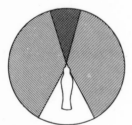

Bird
(pigeon)

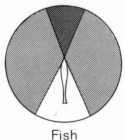

Fish
(trout)

The variable overlap
in the field of vision
of the two eyes.

To our remotest invertebrate ancestors, vision was simply 'phototactic', deriving from scattered pigment spots that registered light and caused the animalcule to swim towards or away from that direction. As these pigment spots became organized into composite 'eyes', which gave a rough mosaic picture of the relative shapes of the objects that lay ahead, they served to identify food or give warning of attacking enemies. From that day on, the separable worlds of the hunter and hunted were born. For throughout the animal kingdom there is a division into those who hunt their prey, who need not fear attack from behind and so can concentrate their visual powers on sharpening their acuity and distance-judgement at the expense of their visual fields, and the hunted, who have no need of sharpened sight for feeding (the grasses they nibble or the plankton of the sea are there for the taking), but who need the widest possible field of vision to allow warning of the shadow of a predator approaching from behind.

The hunters, such as hawks and cats, bring their eyes round to the front of their heads, sacrificing their backward vision and concentrating their optic nerve fibres on a small central patch of the field, common to both eyes, with which they can distinguish the hunted mouse, in spite of his attempts at concealment. The 'hunted', on the other hand, keep their eyes well on the side of their head, and do not concentrate their acuity in the central point of their retinas, since attack may come from any angle; their aim is to have a fairly uniform vision over as much of the 360° field as possible, which will keep them informed of any movement in their wake that might bespeak danger, while they blamelessly graze away.

This dichotomy of hunters and hunted extends on through evolution into the souls of men, except that in the super-evolution of *homo sapiens,* where we no longer need to adapt our anatomy and physiology to our environment, but simply feed more into our cerebral computers, it is the insight rather than the sight that has become more canalized into the rapacious outlook of the human predator, or diffused into the perspectived view of his humane but imposed-on fellow.

Homo sapiens has fields of vision that extend almost exactly to the 180° arc ahead, although the nose and eyebrows restrict the extent of these fields on the inner and upper sides. Many diseases encroach still further on this field of visual awareness, and may correspondingly intrude on the personality, and, in turn, on its artistic projection.

Glaucoma, which is second only to cataract as a cause of blindness in England, is a disease of the ageing in which the intra-ocular fluids cannot seep away quickly enough; the consequent increase of pressure within the eye gradually destroys the retina, characteristically by eroding the more peripheral parts of the visual field. It is a common disease, ultimately affecting nearly a twentieth of the population, but principally from the world of worrying businessmen and politicians (including two recent Prime Ministers). Creative artists are nearly always spared.★

VITREOUS OPACITIES

The simplest intruders into the visual field are the little floating wisps, aptly named 'muscae volitantes' (= flitting flies), that most of us experience at some time, and which occasionally derive from a small haemorrhage into the vitreous chamber. Only rarely do these floating opacities become large or dominant enough to be a distraction. But to the introspective they can attain an even greater reality than the outside world; and such patients may come to feel that their personalities are, as it were, imprisoned, along with their unwelcome but ever-present 'floaters', within the confines of their own eyeball. Thus the Norwegian expressionist, Edvard Munch, an introvert whose paintings reflected much of the alienation of his period, developed a 'haemorrhage' in the vitreous of his better eye at the age of 67, in 1930. The resulting opacity that cast its shadow on the retina, and which had the shape of a bird with a long beak, began to insinuate itself into his paintings as the dominant subject of the world he depicted.

B93
56–58

★ James Joyce's glaucoma was purely secondary to his protracted iritis; and if (as alleged) J. S. Bach had a glaucoma, it was almost certainly secondary to a thrombosis.

B154

Sir Joshua Reynolds, too, developed a vitreous haemorrhage in 1789, when he was 65, and some months later, the other eye also weakened. The doctors called it 'gutta serena', which means little except that on casual inspection they could see no cataract lying white within the pupil. What he probably had was a retinal haemorrhage which then irrupted into the vitreous, since he had already suffered a paralytic stroke seven years earlier.

B123   Two years later, as described by his contemporary biographer, J. Northcote, he 'entertained strong apprehensions concerning the tumour which had been collecting for some time over his left eye' and had latterly been accompanied by much inflammation. The surgeons adopted every means (as they said) to 'discuss' it, but without effect; for it was afterwards discovered to consist merely of extravasated blood, and had no connection with the optic nerve. (They also submitted him to the usual régime of leeches, blisters and heroic doses of mercury, equally without benefit.) Following the advice of his

B28   'most skilful practitioners', he abstained from painting thereafter, hoping to save this remaining eye, 'a determination which cost him great pain'. The following year he died, and as the autopsy revealed only a 'praeternatural enlargement of the liver', Reynolds, like Turner, had possibly succumbed to an alcoholic cirrhosis.

It would have been interesting (in our present context) if his later paintings had shown some characteristic form of colour change – perhaps the yellow-vision of a terminal jaundice from a cirrhotic liver, if not the red-vision resulting from a cataract or from an appropriately placed retinal haemorrhage★ – but ever since his stroke he had put up his prices and farmed out more and more to his pupils, giving only an occasional touch of his own brush to justify the famous sig-

B187   nature and the famous prices. According to Ellis Waterhouse, his red pictures were sometimes attributed to Lawrence and the blue ones to Daniel Gardner, which would still further confuse any attempt at such an organic interpretation.

★ The 'red-vision' resulting from retinal haemorrhage is not often noted, but one artist (N. T.) has recorded that since his macula was damaged by such haemorrhages, his paintings have all become deficient in blue (which he appreciates when this is pointed out to him).

PHOSPHENES

Sometimes there intrude upon the visual field colours, lights and patterns, which are engendered within the retina itself, and are called 'phosphenes'. As children, we are often tantalized by the coloured panorama that is constantly provided for us whenever we shut our eyes, but as adults we tend to ignore this spectacle as our awareness becomes dulled. Only rarely do we manage to see them with the freshness of a child, even if we require a dose of mescaline to achieve this, or re-learn the art, as artists do, of abstracting true colours from the toned-down and conventional colours we normally accept. Sometimes a little pressure on the eyeball helps to provoke such a coloured display. Thus William James noted that 'beautiful patterns, which would do well for wall-papers, succeed each other when the eyeballs are long pressed', and Goethe recorded that he had a constantly recurring phantasm of a flower, whenever he closed his eyes and depressed his head, 'unfolding itself and developing from its interior new flowers, formed of coloured or sometimes green leaves, not natural, but of fantastic forms, and symmetrical as the rosettes of sculptors'.

These coloured 'phosphenes' are often provoked by children who are blind from damaged eyes (retinal dystrophies, congenital cataract, etc.), as opposed to those whose blindness is due to an impediment in the brain and are 'blind to their blindness'. Such children have often been observed to poke their B56, B96 fingers into their orbits, so as to provide a psychedelic substitute for the natural vision from which they are debarred.

Similar bright patterns can be induced by low-grade electrical stimulation of the intact brain, and these have recently been found to show a striking resemblance to the scribblings of young children. Still more significantly, they recall certain neolithic rock drawings, and even hieroglyphic forms. From some 300,000 drawings which pre-school children (of English, American, French, Chinese and Negro origin) start making about the age of 3, Rhoda Kellog identified twenty 'basic B89 scribbles' and six geometrical diagrams, from which the combines and aggregates are constructed that finally lead to the pictorial representation. Out of this, the 'visual alphabet' seems to be formed, which (as opposed to 'language alphabets') is probably common to all humans, regardless of race and culture.

Of a different quality are the little darting specks of light which we sometimes notice ('seeing stars') after a knock on the head

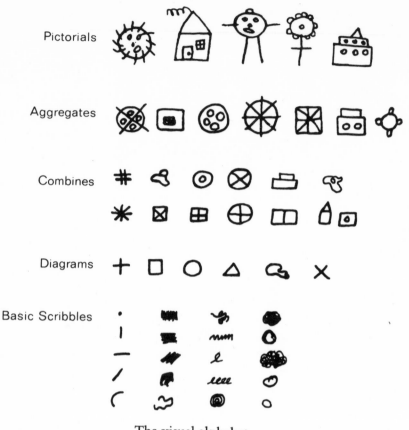

The visual alphabet.

or on suddenly standing up (and thus draining blood from our retinal vessels), and which are attributed uncertainly to the retinal blood corpuscles. To the romantic mind these dancing lights can be decked with angelic vestments or metaphysical meaning. Thus, to the rationalist, the sparkling saints that Joan of Arc witnessed are simply evidence of the lowered pressure in her retinal vessels due to vicarious menstruation, since they appeared at monthly intervals, and we know that she had no normal menstrual flow.

DAMAGE TO THE VISUAL PATHWAYS

Other disorders that encroach on the field of vision derive from progressive damage to the retina, as in retinal detachment, or to the optic nerves as they pass back to imprint the retinal image onto the cerebrum. In the first category falls James Thurber, a high myope, who lost the sight of both eyes from retinal detachments in middle life. He was a man of great courage who, as his remaining eye failed, struggled to continue drawing his cartoons by using black crayons on huge sheets of yellow paper. When his 'fog' became too thick, he stopped sketching and learned to write by dictation, and his delightful fairy tale, *The Thirteen Clocks,* had all the distilled imagery and easy spontaneity of his earlier drawings.

Many have speculated about the cause of Milton's blindness. 5 In a letter to his friend, Leonard Phileras, Milton himself attributed it to 'cataract or amaurosis', since his eyes were not injured 'to outward view'. He even incorporated a play on the Latin name for cataract ('suffusio') and its clinical appearance ('gutta serena') in one of his autobiographical echoes in *Paradise Lost*.[20] Subsequent writers have suggested that his loss of sight was caused by progressive myopia (since both his parents were evidently short-sighted★), albinism (in the egregious company of Tamerlane, Edward the Confessor and Noah), and the universal scapegoat – syphilis (in his case, it was allowed to be congenital). More fanciful diagnoses, very prevalent at the time, attributed his blindness to his political improprieties, and some even averred that it was a drop of the martyred king's blood B20 that 'had quenched his eyes'. However, from Milton's description in this letter of a darkness descending over 'the left part of the left eye', followed by a general restriction of his peripheral vision, retinal detachment and glaucoma were, until recently, B190 considered to be more likely diagnoses.

In fact, it seems that he probably had a pituitary tumour, B148 which could also account for some of the changes in his general health and bearing during the years when his sight was failing, and when the charm and dignity of his earlier works was often replaced (as Mark Pattison put it) by 'the language of the gutter and the fish-market'.

By 1652, when Milton was still only 44 and had twenty-two years more to live, the light had failed completely and his mental

★ Milton's father presumably was myopic, since (as Aubrey describes) he could read without glasses at eighty-four. His mother took to glasses at thirty; they were probably myopic, since astigmatic glasses were not then available, and she is unlikely to have been so hypermetropic that she needed them so early in life.

XXII   Monet *On the Beach, Trouville*, 1870 (detail).

XXIII   Monet *The Japanese Footbridge*, c. 1922.
Monet had cataracts which were ultimately removed. The changes in his colours as well as in the detail of his preceding paintings could be attributed to this.

XXIV   Rouault *The Old King*. The style of Rouault's painting has been likened to the effect of ether on visual perception.

XXV   Wyndham Lewis *Combat Number 3*. Wyndham Lewis gradually lost his field of vision from the inroads of a pituitary tumour.

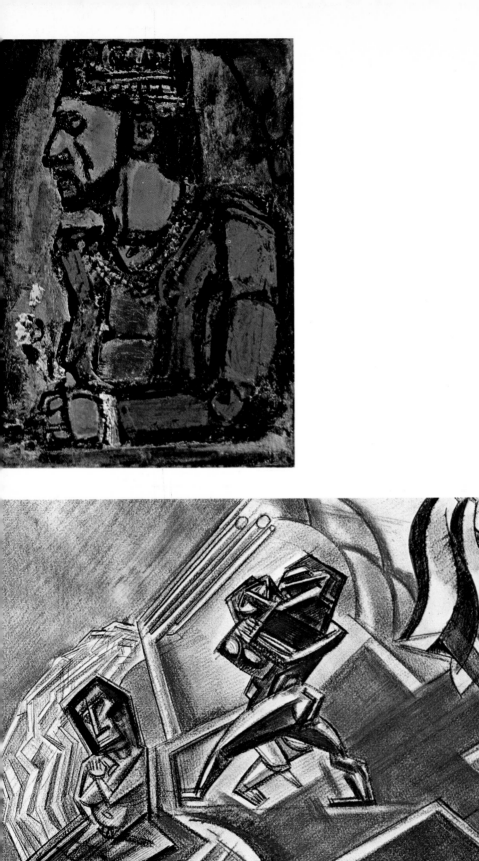

XXVI–XXIX   Louis Wain, paintings of cats made during a schizophrenic illness. The conventional cats depicted by this artist began to fall apart into strange and horrific patterns as his emotional tension mounted, and finally disintegrated into a kaleidoscopic mass.

stability returned. He wrote the sonnet on his blindness (*When I consider how my light is spent/Ere half my days, in this dark world and wide, . . . They also serve, who only stand and wait*); and indeed, the reflection of his blindness keeps recurring in the great poems of his later years – *Eyeless in Gaza, at the mill with slaves* in 'Samson Agonistes'; *But cloud instead, and ever-during dark/Surrounds me* in 'Paradise Lost'. The serenity of his last decades contrasts with the roughness of his middle years. His domestic and political struggles had receded, and a contentment and resignation, that are often encountered in the totally blind, sustained him until his death.

One cannot help marvelling that the whole of 'Paradise Lost', in all its polysyllabic splendour, was written after Milton had lost all useful vision. It seems that he managed to dictate it all in snatches, often of a dozen or so lines, which he usually worked out during his many sleepless nights (wakening his daughter Anna with each inspiration, so that she could commit them to paper). All those harmonies, stresses, caesuras, crowded syllables and pauses that lend the poem its peculiar majesty come from the isolation – perhaps liberation – of his spirit during those early years of total blindness.

XXV

B100

Wyndham Lewis, artist, novelist and critic, began to lose the outer fields of vision of each eye just before the Second World War. He was told by his London oculist that he (like Milton) had a pituitary tumour pressing on the optic nerves, which should be removed. Unhappily the war drove him from England, and his apprehension (but not his sight) was relieved by vitamin injections elsewhere. On his return after the war, the tumour was inevitably much larger, and he was just able to complete the painting of T. S. Eliot in Magdalene, Cambridge, by sitting about six inches away from the canvas, before (as he affectingly described it in *The Listener*), the 'sea-mist' that had been closing in from both sides, reached across the island of sight that remained, and his days of painting were done.[21] At his autopsy only a parcel of nerve-fibres were found to be still surviving the spread of his fatal tumour.[22]

Damage to the fields of vision from pressure still further back along the optic pathways causes a loss, not of the outer fields of both eyes, as with the pituitary tumour, but of the corresponding sides of both eyes, so that the whole of the binocular field – to the left or right (depending on which side of the cerebrum is damaged) – is missing. This is a common sequel to cerebral thrombosis in the elderly, and such patients, being usually unaware of their blindness may subconsciously fill in the missing half-field with a picture, such as would seem a natural continuation of the seen half-field on the unaffected side. In the well-ordered psyche, such a covering over of the defect may give a welcome feeling of security; although this may be rudely interrupted by meeting unanticipated obstacles in the blind half-field, or when reading into the blind area is found to be as frustrating as trying to read pages in a dream. To the unquiet mind, however, this empty canvas is asking for trouble, and into it can be deposited all the embarrassing memories and refuse that the ego has been trying so hard to obliterate. L. Savin has described how the blind half-field in such a 'homonymous hemianopia' may become colonized by imagined strangers who remorselessly gesticulate, and from whom there is no escape, or by freakish and mischievous intruders that may plague the aged arteriosclerotic, especially if his conscience is unclear.[23] And fanciful interpreters attribute the malign figures of Brueghel and Bosch to such a vascular mishap.   B153

It has even been suggested that the scintillating haloes borne by so many medieval saints, and even the very steps of Jacob's ladder, were simply projections of the auras of an attack of migraine (which is known to stem from a similar restriction of the blood-supply to the brain). In the case of St Hildegard   62
there is probably some truth in this, since she describes in detail how the visions, which she painted so vividly afterwards, were preceded by waving lights or flames, often with definite 'fortification figures' and radiating from a coloured area (as do the classical 'scintillating scotomas' of migraine). And her descriptions should certainly not be dismissed lightly, since Hildegard was not just an ecstatic abbess, but a writer of science with an analytical approach unique in her period, for she was born in AD 1098, when the 'science' of the dark ages had barely emerged   B161
into the Arabian twilight.[24]

Damage to the nerve-fibres that pass backwards from the eye can also be caused by poisons within the bloodstream; and some of these, such as tobacco, may have a selective effect on our colour responses, causing a patch in the field of vision with diminished awareness of red and green. Thus of Maurice Greiffenhagen (RA, 1862–1931) it is said that his excessive fondness for tobacco caused such a central 'colour scotoma' in his final years, to which his later paintings bear testimony.

PSYCHEDELIC ART

The impact of other poisons falls on our visual nerve-fibres almost at the end of their long journey from the retina to the point in the brain where a conscious visual 'percept' emerges. Mescaline and other hallucinogenic drugs seem to cause an interruption of the 'association fibres' in the posterior lobe of the brain, which mould the unconscious cerebral image of the seen world into the conscious percept, altering it, in the light of our experience and needs, so that it falls into line with our established schemas, with all the attributes that we think proper for the object we now recognize. Mescaline thus allows us to see a far truer image than the ordered stereotype that our association-fibres normally permit us to apprehend. It lets us see the true shadow-colours – the blue shadow in the snow, the green beneath the red object, and so on, that we normally discountenance; for we can cope with the flux of our complex external world only if objects remain what we expect them to be, if snow is always white and houses are always vertical, irrespective of the tilt of the eye and the slope of the retinal image.

The effect of mescaline on vision seems usually to fall into three phases, although such purely subjective experiences necessarily vary with the individual, the dose and the environment. The first, and the most enjoyable, is an escape from the dulling effect of familiarity, which allows a gradual heightening of the colours around us and an emergence of the shadow-colours, which we normally suppress and ignore. Together with this comes an increased awareness of the third dimension; for, again, we have become accustomed to ignore the blurring of distant objects when we focus for near, and vice-versa; mescaline permits no such deceptive covering up of our limited depth of focus, any more than it permits one to smudge over the true colours we see. And so objects seem to attain a 'solidity' that enhances their quality and interest. As Aldous Huxley* described it:

B78

* Aldous Huxley became nearly blind in adolescence from keratitis, which led to gross scarring of both corneas. This cleared to a limited extent during the next decades, and Huxley rashly gave credit for this natural clearance to a bogus system of eye-exercises that he had been persuaded to practise, before the sight again worsened (as is usual in this type of keratitis) in his later years.

. . . the perspective looked rather odd and the walls of the room no longer seemed to meet at right-angles. But these were not the really important facts. The really important facts were that spatial relationships had ceased to matter very much and that my mind was perceiving the world in terms of other than spatial categories. . . . What I noticed, what impressed itself upon my mind, was the fact that all [the books] glowed with living light and that in some the glory was more manifest than in others.

The awareness of the rediscovery of the beauty in those parts of the visual scene which had previously been taken for granted, or whose less strident colours had been overlooked or even frankly suppressed, is again recalled by Huxley:

A moment later a clump of red hot pokers, in full bloom, had exploded into my field of vision. So passionately alive that they seemed to be standing on the very brink of utterance, the flowers strained upwards into the blue. Like the chair under the table, they protested too much. I looked down at the leaves and discovered a cavernous intricacy of the most delicate green lights and shadows, pulsing with indecipherable mystery.

> Roses:
> The flowers are easy to paint,
> The leaves difficult.

Shiki's Haiku expresses, by indirection, exactly what I then felt – the excessive, the too obvious glory of the flowers, as contrasted with the subtler miracle of their foliage.

It may be an hour later before the second stage of mescaline-intoxication becomes prominent, and it signals the increasing suppression of those other associations that relate us to the external world. We begin to mistrust the interpretations we make of all the images we are seeing. We no longer compensate for the shifting positions of the retinal image as we rotate our eyes, and thus the objects around us seem to jump about, in time with the movements of the retinal image; hence the jazzy and repetitive quality of some of the paintings executed under the influence of mescaline. And again, since the room we see is no longer our familiar room, with every object safely identifiable from its past associations, but a series of colours and patterns and contours, which assume far more relevance than the mere function and history of the objects to which these shapes and colours relate.

The final phase follows when the progressive dulling of the associations that bind us to our sensory environment renders that environment less and less real. Fear mounts as the schizophrenia deepens; then, as the toxic effects of the drug begin to wane, a new security seems to return, and we gradually resume our earthly mantle; but the heady memories of our immortality remain, for we have seen the true colours, the true contours and the true perspectives, which with a conscious effort we can recall and enjoy for the rest of time.

These truths that underlie our seen world, and which we habitually ignore, are indeed the stock-in-trade of so many great painters, who have not needed mescaline to disclose what is there for anyone with perspicacity to apprehend. The brilliant and contrasting shadow-colours have been deployed by Impressionists and Post-Impressionists for nearly a century. The heightened sense of perspective that gives a three-dimensional quality to the central subject has been utilized at any rate since Renaissance painters like Bronzino. The emphasis of contours and structural content recalls particularly some contemporary paintings, such as those of Merlyn Evans. The jazzy repetitions and the whirling movements of the images recall the vorticism of Wyndham Lewis. And the whole gamut of visual novelties has been popularized in the current vogue for psychedelic art.

XXV

SCHIZOPHRENIC ART

There are certain parallels between the visual world and artistry of the natural schizophrenic and those of the schizoid state induced by mescaline. The 'perseveration' or repetitions of a sharp visual image, so that it spills on to the succeeding images or 'jazzes' its way across the scene as the eyes rotate – a characteristic hallucination after taking mescaline (which is simply caused by a heightened and prolonged formation of our normal 'after-images') – is echoed in the fragmentations and in the reduplication of the figures in many schizophrenic paintings.

Some schizophrenic artists achieve a bizarre and dream-like quality that is the envy of many surrealists. Others, with visual and verbal imagery overlapping, interpolate words or phrases into their paintings, which again have the dream-like quality of being slightly off-true, or even become fabricated neo-

logisms. And others, concentrating on elaboration and stylization, lose the representation in a mosaic of colours, just as the
conventional cats of Louis Wain began to fall apart into strange
and horrific patterns as his emotional tension mounted, and
finally disintegrated into a kaleidoscopic mass.

XXVI–XXIX

Indeed for many schizophrenics, painting has served as a
safety-valve, with which to externalize their confusion or
despair; and in many cases the exotic or compulsive renderings
of their distraught psyche are far more 'artistic' than the tame
products of their more balanced past. Thus, in the case of one
artist who was recently subjected to a frontal leucotomy, her
timid post-operation renderings are a pale echo of the fever
and brilliance of those from a less contented past.

But in the case of those whose dementia permits little release
of emotion, and who withdraw from the outer world, their
paintings provide a clinical rather than an aesthetic interest.
Their strokes may become tinier and tinier, till their contact
with reality suffices only to let them make a few dots on the
paper. Occasionally this shrinkage of the point of contact means
that their whole world is shrinking; indeed, occasionally, it is
they themselves who seem to be shrinking, as in Alice's Won-
derland. One such patient described how his sudden self-
shrinkings could only be stemmed by grasping objects that
would relate his dimensions to the outside world. Again the
depression of such schizophrenics often shows itself by a
curtailment of the scene they are depicting to a series of basic
forms that simply express their negativism and apathy, such as
a hard empty horizon or the blank implacable zig-zag of a
mountain-range.

In general, the preferences of schizophrenics are for tactile
rather than visual sensations (which is also found to be true in
'only' children). Visual hallucinations are rare, by comparison
with auditory and tactile ones, because vision is essentially a
distance-sense and readily abstracted, while the near-senses, of
touch and hearing, that entail 'involvement', become disturbed
when their contact with the external world is lost.

B157

GROSS LOSS OF VISUAL FIELD –
NEAR-BLIND ART

When the loss of visual field is so extensive that only an occasional
island of sight remains, drawing or painting may still be possible,
in that the pencil can be seen to contact the paper; but these

hardly count as visual arts, since the whole conception is essentially one of feeling rather than sight. Such near-blind artists, being released from the constraints of direct representation, are thrust into that haptic or kinaesthetic world that opens up a whole new system of. values and a whole new pattern of imagery.

B104, B105

In his school of blind and near-blind children in Philadelphia, Professor Victor Lowenfeld has encouraged his pupils to make capital out of their limitations, and a remarkable series of drawings has emerged. These emphasize the individual shapes that are interesting to the children – symbolically, haptically (for the quality of its texture and contours), and kinaesthetically (for its movement potential).

68–70

The three drawings illustrated on page 142 were the successive expressions of a boy whose congenital cataracts permitted him to see only an area of about $2\frac{1}{2}$ inches in diameter on his drawing-board. He had no knowledge of the overall contours of the head that he was depicting, and in this way he was like the blind sculptor who envisages a head as the sum of a multitude of small areas which he can map out with his fingers.

The particular interest of these three successive drawings is that they clearly illustrate the three stages of development that Lowenfeld described for all who are primarily subjective or 'autoplastic' interpreters, and who are spared from having their natural haptic evaluations overlaid by the influence of good vision. The earliest stage is the diffuse representation of the whole image – apparently naturalistic because of its undifferentiated character: this he described as the 'stage of self-confrontation'. Then, after a while, comes a gradual appreciation of the separate elements of form and expression. 'This second stage of development at some point becomes such an overwhelming discovery that it overpowers his whole concept; instead of our first, vaguely formulated, projection, we now have a structural overemphasis of the meaningful parts. The second stage then appears of almost geometric character, since the structural element has become vitally significant in the discovery and formulation of the self'. Only when the child has experienced the intellectual and emotional power to express his imagery, does he move on to the third stage in which, as we see, the rigid structural and symbolic formulation gives way to a more flexible expression of his visual and haptic experiences.

56–58   Edvard Munch's late paintings show the intrusion of a
bird-shaped vitreous opacity.

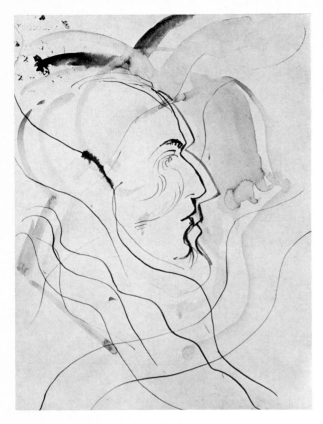

59–61   Drawings under the influence of LSD
25 by L. Matéfy.

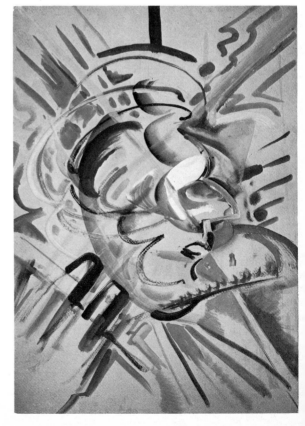

62   St Hildegard, whose visions have been analyzed as the fortification spectra of an attack of migraine.

63   Harpist invoking Horus, whose symbol was the eye.

64   Mithras, one of the many ancient gods associated with the sun.

65   Oedipus plucking out his eyes.

66 Head of Siva. The third eye was normally
kept closed, as it would burn up anything it saw.

67 Tintoretto, *Susanna and the Elders*. The classical voyeurs inviting retribution.

68–70 Paintings by a congenitally near-blind boy.
(68) first stage of 'self-confrontation'; pseudo-realistic
representation: (69) second stage of 'structural
discovery'; geometric forms: (70) third stage of 'free
structural variation'; discovery of style (Above).

74–76 Sculpture by a ⟶
blind girl: *Deserted,
Mourning,* and *Woman
Talking.*

71–73 Sculptures by a congenitally blind boy. (71) first
stage of 'self-confrontation'; (72) second stage of
'structural discovery'; (73) third stage of 'free structural
variation' (Below).

77 Pieter Brueghel,
Parable of the Blind.
Brueghel has been labelled
the 'arch-diagnostician of
eye ailments', because of
his frequent illustration
of the different types of
blindness.

78 St Lucy, the patron
saint of ophthalmology,
who, in remorse, plucked
out her eyes. God gave her
two replacements.

glasses simply to screen their guilt from the penetrating looks
of their fellows.[29]

The common practice nowadays of wearing ordinary spectacles that correct a trifling refractive error (which was not,
itself, causing symptoms) is equally said by psychologists to be
evidence of the demand for such protective shields for the
guiltful or self-conscious soul. Some eye surgeons, more
dedicated to the psychoanalytical approach, regard the glass
of such spectacles as the symbolic equivalent of the hymen and
hold that the use of virtually plain-glass spectacles indicates a
need to retrieve a lost virginity.★

Since the eye is thus the vehicle to sex, blindness is the
traditional punishment for sexual licence. Oedipus pierced his
eyes after discovering his incest, and the intrusive young men
of Sodom were blinded for their alleged designs against the
visiting angels. Peeping Tom was blinded through looking at
the naked (and exhibitionistic) Godiva; Tiresias the soothsayer
had been blinded because he had seen Athene bathing naked;
and the threat of blindness was, and perhaps still is, the age-old
deterrent to the masturbating schoolboy.[30] Schizophrenics,
burdened with sex-guilt, have on many occasions removed
either their testicles or their eyes, as vehicles for their shameful
needs. And St Lucy, the patron saint of ophthalmology,   78
tore out both her eyeballs, because she had looked on a man
lustfully. (God, in His wisdom, subsequently gave her two replacements.)†

★ More than half of the American population over the age of five
wear glasses, and, of these, women outnumber men in every category.
Sometimes these spectacles are justified by the wearer on the basis
of the myth that the eye can be damaged by not wearing glasses or
by wearing incorrect ones. In fact the eye itself can never be damaged
in this way. The only occasion where glasses may help to prevent
impairment of sight is in the rare squint amblyopia of small children,
where the lowered vision is due to changes in the brain (comparable
to hysterical blindness) and not in the eye.

† The Scottish equivalent, Saint Triduana, sent her offending eyes
on a skewer to her lustful admirer, and the Irish equivalent, Saint
Medana, plucked out her eyes and threw them at the feet of her ardent
lover.

The most curious and widespread development of this relationship between God, the eye, and sex is found in the concept of the Evil Eye – one of the oldest and most prevalent superstitions in history, reaching from ancient Assyria* to present-day Sicily, and from India to Peru, with the swastika constantly reappearing as the protecting symbol.† The Evil Eye was generally a perquisite of women until the last century, when it was even attributed to popes (such as Pius IX and Leo XIII) and to kings (such as Alfonso XIII). The Hindu God Siva had an evil third eye in the centre of his forehead, which was normally kept closed, as it would burn up anything it looked at, whereas the Medusa's turned all to stone. The basilisk[31] (a sort of hooded cobra) and the cockatrice (which had been incubated by a toad from the egg of an elderly cock) were the animal equivalents.

Throughout its history the evil eye (like witchcraft) has always been related to sex, both in the 'caster' and the recipient. As Antony of Carthagena (1611) said, 'Old women can fascinate more easily because the menstrual blood is retained in their veins,' and the glance of a menstruating woman is believed by South African bushmen to turn men into trees, and among certain American Indians, menstruating women are required to leave the camp, the only antidote to their glances being to protect oneself behind the forefingers crossed in the pattern of a swastika. In the recipient, the especial power of the evil eye was to destroy fertility, with periods of particular vulnerability at the sexual climacterics of circumcision, puberty, marriage and childbirth.

Small wonder, then, that throughout history the blind have been regarded as damned, paying the penalty for some sexual failing – in themselves, or in their fathers before them, or,

B65

* King Ashurbanapal of Nineveh (668–626 BC) had incantations available with which he could combat the dangerous glances of his Assyrian witches.

† The Caduceus, carried by Mercury, was also a protecting symbol, initially designed to shield him from the evil eye of Juno. By a confusion with the emblem of Aesculapius (a single serpent on a staff), it was adopted as the badge of the medical profession by Sir William Butts, physician to King Henry VIII.

among Hindus, of their previous incarnations. As such, they
were relegated to the lowest social status, any attempt to better
them being held as an impious intervention in God's judgment.★ Thus the blind remain through history as ineducable
mendicants, beneath any social status, and only coming to the
fore when their sightless eyes were replaced by an inner vision.
The famous soothsayers of history and fable have, in the main,
had their prophetic eyes liberated by their blindness. As Milton
put it: *Blind Thamyris and blind Meonides* [= Homer] *And
Tiresias and Phineas, prophets old.*[32] To these may be added
Blind Bartimeus, who recognized Jesus as Messiah, and Appius
Claudius, who warned the Roman Senate of disaster if they
came to terms with Pyrrhus. Democritus, the laughing philo-
sopher of Abdera, even eviscerated his eyes so that he might
think more clearly; while a similar pseudo-castration was
suggested by certain Fathers of the Church, on the grounds   B54
that a vision of the next world was preferable to vision in this.
Wotan, who drank from Mimir's fountain in order to become
the wisest of gods, had to sacrifice one eye in the process.
(Wagner, perhaps subconsciously adding the sexual motif,
gave Wotan his wife Fricka as a further recompense for the
loss of his eye.) Horus, who had lost an eye in his fight with Set,
had it restored by Thoth, the God of Wisdom: thus his eye
became the symbol of sacrifice and offering, and acquired
magical powers.

Rarely in history was a humane thought given to the armies
of blind beggars that languished in every kingdom. Sometimes
they were execrated, as in the edict of King David, who said,
'Whosoever getteth up to the father, and smiteth the Jebusites,
and the lame and the blind, that are hated of David's soul, He
shall be Chief and Captain' (II Samuel, 5, 8). Other despots
simply augmented them: e.g. the Byzantine Emperor Basil
('The Bulgar-Slayer') sent back his 15,000 prisoners, every man
blinded, to their king (who died of the shock). And in England
blinding was introduced in AD 600 as an alternative to the death
penalty. St Louis let humanity prevail when he founded the
'Quinze-Vingts' in 1260 (which is still functioning as the 'Asile

★ Only in Japan was this apparently modified, the blind being allowed
a special status, although low in the general hierarchy.

des Aveugles'); but it was not until the advent of the Enlighten-
ment in the late eighteenth century that the possibility of
assisting, educating and even curing the blind was seriously
considered. Louis Braille suggested his revolutionary script in
1835 (originally as an aid to blind musicians), although it was
thirty years in gaining acceptance; and after that the blessings
of the mechanical age poured in, until now, with talking-
books, typewriters, wireless, telephones and a hundred other
devices, a full, useful and rewarding life is at last open to the
blind.

PSYCHOLOGY AND ART OF THE BLIND

Along with all this came an irresistible fascination with the
psychology of the blind, for whom new hospitals, charities
and societies were emerging. This interest was heightened by
the impact of Freudian lore, which established the peculiar
importance of our eyes and sight in the evolution of our
personalities. Until the turn of the century, there were constant
references to the blind man's development of extra senses that
could divine colours in cloth, project the sense of touch beyond
arm's length, and make it possible to feel radiations that
ordinary mortals never know. Indeed the more fanciful of the
blind – perhaps in whimsy, perhaps in despair – would sometimes encourage these investigations by talking of the obscure
skin contractions experienced as they approached obstacles.
But reason gradually prevailed, and it became apparent that
the blind did little more than concentrate their attention and
awareness.[33] The old concept is, nevertheless, far from dead
in the popular mind, and the recent publicity given to Rosa
Kuleshova who claimed to recognize colours and read print
through her fingertips – even when felt through layers of
metal or glass – gave an impetus to that improbable theory of
B39   'dermo-optical perception' which had been floated by Jules
Romains some forty years ago.[34] Rosa subsequently found
that she could read equally well through her toes, and then
through her elbow. These claims were later exposed, but
others had meanwhile taken her cue; in the USSR she was
followed by Ninel Kulagina and Lena Bliznova, and even in
sceptical New York, twenty girls from Barnard College joined
the ranks of the dermo-optical perceivers. Others have followed,
but somehow the world remains unconvinced, and no evidence
B57   has been found of thermal and textual clues on which this

egregious capacity could be based.★ The notion that our other senses are enhanced by our blindness is still well-established in relation to hearing, and even to smell, for we know that blind camel-drivers are highly esteemed, since the smell of the earth gives guidance in the desert where sight is often of little avail.

In general, the established blind betray a patient scepticism when determined psychologists attempt to dissect their attitudes, categorize their failings and generalize about their special psychopathology. They say (with justice) that they are but ordinary men with the ordinary proportions of personality patterns, to whom blindness is just an inconvenient accident. Margery Fry's comment, that 'to the administrator an individual may be just "that old woman: I think her name is Jones", but to herself she is Katie Jones who won a prize for scripture and had the smallest waist in her class – with a thousand other distinctive features – who just happens to be old', applies with equal force to the blind and partially-sighted population.†

B58

Nevertheless, these diverse personalities tend to be given a cloak of uniformity, fashioned partly by our concept of how a blind person should behave and partly by the blind person's own acceptance of an attitude that seems appropriate to the minority group to which he now belongs. Thus, just as we generalize about the volatile Frenchman, the stolid Teuton and

★ It is true that light-sensitive pigments are present in the skin of many animals, mainly aquatic forms with non-waterproof skins; but such a dermal light-sense is very rare in terrestial arthropods, cephalopods and amniotes. These pigment spots have no fundamental difference from true eyes, with which they may co-exist (having similar photo-chemical systems), and they may serve to control locomotion, even in some lower vertebrates.

† One recalls the garden of specially-scented flowers created in 1968 in Regents Park, London, for the delectation of the blind (their Institute lies hard-by). The intent was not well received, blind commentators emphasizing that their main wish was to be integrated into society as inconspicuously as possible, and that they had little interest in these gardens which would merely serve to accentuate their segregation.

the operatic Italian, so we have our ready image of the heroic★ or pathetic blind; and into this mould we tend to press the blind personalities we meet, so that the blind man is inevitably drawn to act up to his established image.

To the more sensitive psyche this rather spurious role may seem distasteful, and, if the blind person has not the discipline and forbearance to maintain his integrity, he may well relapse into a vegetable existence within his sheltered employment, or even withdraw, a little soured or defiant, into a world of his own. Happily these negative or antisocial responses are rare, because the blind man is forced to open himself to his fellows; he is dependent on their conversation and help for nearly everything he does. Privacy is difficult to sustain when one's most intimate actions may well need supervision if not actual assistance, or indeed may be observed without one's knowledge. The blind man tends to become increasingly responsive, since his whole orientation depends on constant communication with his fellows; should he start as an intelligent introvert, this secondary extroversion that he accomplishes may yield a personality-amalgam approaching the ideal.

This situation contrasts strikingly with the predicament of the deaf, whose difficulty in communication forces them to retreat into a world of their own. Resentment at the evident embarrassment their company causes is combined with suspicion that they are being deceived or maligned in the conversations they cannot comprehend; and a secondary introversion furthers their retreat. Small wonder that the blind are popular. They excite sympathy and admiration, and they figure again and again in literature as repositories for our sentimental needs, while one would search long to find a hero or heroine in fiction who was deaf or dumb.

When the sight is suddenly lost, there will inevitably follow a period in which shock, despair, defiance, over-compensation and acceptance succeed one another. Thereafter it is just a matter of making the extra efforts of awareness and adaptation,

★ Sometimes his heroism is carried almost to excess, as in the case of John the Blind king of Bohemia, who bravely led his troops on the field of Crécy; or Blind Bayard, the legendary steed given to Rinaldo by Charlemagne, which is still apparently to be heard neighing and snorting in the Ardennes on Midsummer Night.

and learning to live within one's new confines. It is the limitation of physical freedom that is perhaps the most exacting, for few blind people ever venture beyond the safety of their home or place of work. Yet they rarely yearn for the recovery of their sight. Once these adjustments have been made, they find it hard to face the further battle of re-adapting to a seeing world. J. F. Wilson described how he was once subjected to some tests based on Romains' theory that pigment spots within the skin can be developed as a substitute for normal vision. He says that he desisted, 'not because these tests appeared tiresome and un-productive, but because concentration on the prospect of re-gaining my sight caused me a good deal of mental disturbance.' He also quoted one of his blind colleagues who, at the age of sixteen, refused to co-operate in treatment which might have brought him some sight, simply because he could not face the consequences of its success. Ophthalmologists are often re-minded of this paradox. The least grateful patients are generally those whose cataracts have been removed and whose sight has been dramatically restored. They grumble endlessly at the in-evitable but transient distortions caused by cataract-spectacles. If they are old and have settled back into a comfortable depend-ence on others, it is upsetting to be told that they must fend for themselves again. A third of the blind in England are sightless because of a senile cataract that could well be removed, but they have somehow failed to have recourse to this straight-forward sight-saving operation, often, one suspects, because they cannot face the business of readjusting to a sighted world.

B192

Whereas those who once had good sight will retain through their years of blindness a concept of space, distance, colours and perspective, even if these become rendered down and formalized as time passes, the blind-from-birth can conceive objects only in terms of three dimensions, embellished by qualities of texture and significance. Such a conception is usually stable and precise, admitting little ambiguity or illusion.★

B192

★ Diderot gives the following comment from his blind companion: 'If it were not for curiosity, I would just as soon have long arms; it seems to me my hands would tell me more of what goes on in the moon than your eyes or your telescopes; and, besides, eyes cease to see sooner than hands to touch.'

As J. F. Wilson puts it, 'The primary object of a tactual conception must necessarily be small enough to be felt. Blind people differ in their ability to correlate single tactual concepts imaginatively into something like a tactual "scene". Undoubtedly, some are able to build up a tri-dimensional picture of a very large object from its single, feelable components'; and he quotes the following lines from a poem entitled *Tough Landscape* by the late W. H. Coates, who was blind from birth, as a remarkable example of that ability exceptionally developed:

B32

Then stepped my fancy out over the scene.
Through stiff bracken she waded,
The turf caressed her feet,
The ground flowed away in broad slopes towards the valley.

She heard the shadow-sound of trees;
Her hands brushed the fields — a thousand acres —
To touch the distant wood
Flung like a scarf of lace
Upon the knees of the hills.

She buried her face in grasses rich and cool
When to the plain she leapt
Beside a level river —
A polished strip of metal cutting the pastures.

And thence to farther hills
Swelling beneath my disembodied hands
In three-dimensional curves:
Most lovely hills, phantom and far away
And overlaid with velvet.

And farther yet, beyond the misty hills,
I reached the wrinkled sea;
I touched the waves with crests of thistledown.

Objects too large to be encompassed by the hands and arms are more often conceived by a process of imagination which reduces them to touchable size, or by the blind subject projecting himself, as it were, into the situation conceived. These two methods are exemplified by the following answers from two men blind from birth, when asked by Wilson how they would picture a battleship shooting at an attacking aeroplane. The Reducer replied: 'At first my mind will register only a confusion of noises such as the BBC Effects Department would produce for such an occasion. But, when I get past that, I find that what I am actually doing is something like producing a puppet show. The battleship, a spiky toy affair, such as I played with in my bath as a child, and the aeroplane diving to the attack in proportion. I am following its descent with my cupped hands as I might the flight of a wasp.' The Projector replied: 'I don't conceive the whole thing, such as a battleship, ever. It's more the case of me on the bridge, me in a turret, me walking along a corridor below the water-line. Picturing a train, I may occasionally think of it as a trembling arrow of sound that hurls itself through the station, setting everything a-quiver and gone in a flash. More often it would be me in a compartment with no sense of the whole train beyond the rhythm and movement of the carriage.'

Of these two responses, the first permits but a weak grasp of objective reality, whereas the second can hardly be called objective at all. Both are sadly lacking in the grandeur and richness of visual imagery.

B192, B32

Wilson also quotes another of Coates' (unpublished) poems as the most successful attempt he knows to translate visual terms into tactile imagery. Here he has taken a stanza from Shelley's *Prometheus Unbound* (in which the nymph Asia is watching the dawn break over the mountains), which is loaded with visual images; nevertheless the tactile vocabulary never fails, and the result is far above the simple exercise of a translator's skill:

Shelley (*Prometheus Unbound,* Act II, line 19):

> The point of one white star is quivering still
> Deep in the orange light of widening morn
> Beyond the purple mountains: through a chasm
> Of wind-divided mist the darker lake
> Reflects it; now it wanes: it gleams again
> As the waves fade, and as the burning threads
> Of woven cloud unravel in pale air:
> 'Tis lost! And through yon peaks of cloudlike snow
> The roseate sunlight quivers: . . .

Coates' 'translation':

> One cold metallic grain is quivering still
> Deep in the flood of warm ethereal fluid
> Beyond the velvet mountains: through a chasm
> In banks of fleece the heavier lake is splashed

With flakes of fiery foam; it wanes: it grows
As the waves thicken, and as the burning threads
Of woven wool unravel in tepid air;
'Tis lost! And through the unsubstantial snow
Of yonder peaks quivers the living form
And vigour of the sun: . . .

This verbal imagery of the blind has all the fascination of an Alice-in-Wonderland world, where everything is strange yet recognizable and true, and sometimes no less beautiful. But it would be wrong to infer that much blind writing is of this high order; the blind have little chance to comprehend the beauties and subtleties of sighted literature, whose references and images must so often be without meaning, and they have had no tradition of tactile-writing on which to build their style or from which to furnish their stock of symbols. For the blind, our vocabulary has been stripped of many of its richest descriptive words and phrases, and none have been added in their place. In learning to keep afloat in a bustling, sighted world, so much else must be mastered, so much extra time and effort is absorbed by the simplest tasks, that the energy to create new symbols and metaphors, and to learn how best to deploy them, is more than can be expected of all but the fortunate and gifted few.

It would be a pity to leave the literature of the blind without reference to the most famous of all blind poets – Homer. But the theory of his blindness is based very insecurely on a single 'Homeric hymn', in which the writer speaks personally of himself as 'a blind man, and he lives in rocky Chios'. It is supported (equally insecurely) by Homer's sparse and apparently contradictory use of visual images and colour names (e.g. black [μέλαν] is applied to blood, new-ploughed earth, water, ships, wine, and so on; but this seeming confusion is common in Greek literature – see page 63); and in any case a single authorship of the Homeric writings is most unlikely. However, some further support for a 'blind Homer' has recently been claimed by psychological analysis of Homer's dream sequences. For it would appear that they carry the same elements and follow the same patterns as do the dreams of the blind, indicating (at any rate to the analyst) that Homer lost his sight at an early age.

In musical composition, the same sort of problems and physical impediments face the blind as in creative writing, unless, of course, the blindness comes on only in middle life, as in the case of Delius or in old age with both Bach and Handel[35] who, like their literary counterpart Milton, had reached their creative maturity in a sighted world. The blind often make excellent musicians, but the difficulty of reading by touch and memorizing a score usually limits their prowess to a solo *tour de force*,[36] or to accompanying their own songs – like the blind Demodocus, who beguiled Odysşeus as he lingered at the court of Alcinous.

If, for the blind who are creative, music is difficult and painting clearly impossible, sculpture at least provides an ample outlet.

In the last chapter we noted how a gradual restriction of the field of vision could sometimes liberate the young artist from the constraints imposed by a convention that required a near-photographic likeness of the subject he was trying to depict, and allowed him increasingly to emphasize the features that were to him most relevant. The blind artist, having no such constraint, can express his feelings for the subject as soon as he has learnt to control his medium.

The three illustrations on page 142 show very well the stages in evolution of the sculpture of a boy who had been blind from birth, and compare interestingly with the drawings of the partially-sighted boy (page 142). He starts with the sculptural equivalent of the first crudely realistic stage (although the head in this case is fashioned facing away from its creator). This is followed by the same second stage of structural discovery, with great over-emphasis of the seemingly significant features, vaguely geometrical, and equivalent to neolithic art in many of its more mature representations. And there is the same final stage, when the blind sculptor freely expresses his experiences by introducing new elements of form, or by varying his own structural symbols.

The concept of an autonomous 'haptic' sense, that allows the apprehension of form and space independently of optics and acoustics, is not difficult to accept, and this may simply lie buried beneath the visual assessment in all but those who are born blind. But (as V. Lowenfeld has maintained) for a minority, the haptic sense remains the primary orientation. Such people interpret their world by touch, by their bodily feelings and by their muscular sensations, and their art is thus essentially 'expressionistic', in contrast to the visually-motivated majority

B104, B105

who tend to paint in more realistic style.

The awareness that this separate haptic evaluation may have its own aesthetic came to the fore after the First World War, when a group of French sculptors encouraged blindfolding in order to emphasize the three-dimensional quality of their renderings by excluding all visual perception. Thereafter the totally blind were encouraged to express themselves in sculpture, and the images that have been produced during the ensuing decades are full of interest and appeal. But there is still the essential question of whether the achievements of blind sculptors are determined by autonomous haptic principles, or correspond to our own aesthetic norms; and this problem (in B140 spite of the extensive investigations of G. Révész) remains unanswered.

Just as the fundamental basis of aesthetics still remains an enigma, the whole underlying pattern of how we integrate our percepts is still far from solved. This latter issue has long excited interest among philosophers, and since philosophy in the grand sense no longer exists, psychoanalysts, replacing the lapidary language of Locke by a formidable jargon of their own, have sustained the inquiry with redoubled zest.

B103 Locke had first raised this issue in 1690 when, based on the observations of his blind Dublin companion, Molyneux, he decided that the idea of space must be a simple idea that could be indiscriminately 'let into the mind' either by sight or touch – or by both simultaneously. Such a unitary concept was ques-

B15 tioned by Berkeley (in his *New Theory of Vision*) in 1709, who argued that sight was truly concerned only with 'light and colours' and our notions of space were acquired solely from the moving, extended bodies 'in circumambient space'; and although Locke's view generally prevailed, it now seems that Berkeley reached nearer to the truth. It could be added that in Eastern Europe the motor theory (that 'Touch teaches Vision') prevails, since it is found more compatible with Marxist–Leninist philosophy. Nevertheless, our vision dominates our B147 touch, even re-shaping it; and, when the two are in conflict, vision wins.

THE RECOVERY OF SIGHT

The recovery of sight, and the complex process by which a man born blind and well adapted in a world of touch and sound, learns to re-evaluate his world in terms of sight, is one that has always fascinated those who have witnessed its slow evolution. It has, incidentally, provided a frequent *coup-de-théâtre* for novels, films and stage, particularly since the advent of corneal grafting. Such fictional accounts were not bothered with the need for accuracy, as the dramatic moment required an almost immediate recognition of all one's surroundings, and in particular of all the more romantic members of the cast.

The first scientific assessment of how one 'learns to see' was made by the pioneer eye-surgeon, William Cheselden, in the Philosophical Transactions of 1728; to his account, exemplary in its clarity and concision, the rather archaic phraseology of his time lends an added charm, which makes it difficult to resist quoting him at some length:

B30

An account of observations made by a young gentleman who was born blind, or lost his sight so early that he had no remembrance of ever having seen, and was couch'd between thirteen and fourteen years of age.

. . . who, though he knew these colours asunder in a good light, yet when he saw them after he was couch'd, the faint ideas he had of them before, were not sufficient for him to know them by afterwards, and therefore he did not think them the same which he had before known by those names. Now scarlet he thought the most beautiful of all colours, and of others the most gay were the most pleasing; whereas the the first time he saw black it gave him great uneasiness, yet after a little time he was reconciled to it; but some months after, seeing by accident a Negro woman, he was struck with great horror at the sight.

When he first saw, he was so far from making any judgment about distances, that he thought all objects whatever touch'd his eyes (as he express'd it) as what he felt did his skin, and thought no objects so agreeable as those which were smooth and regular, though he could form no judgment of their shape, or guess what it was in any object that was pleasing to him: He knew not the shape of any thing, nor any one thing from another, however different in shape or magnitude;

159

but upon being told what things were, whose form he before knew from feeling, he would carefully observe, that he might know them again; but having too many objects to learn at once, he forgot many of them; and (as he said) at first he learned to know, and again forgot a thousand things in a day. One particular only, though it may appear trifling, I will relate: Having often forgot which was the cat, and which the dog, he was asham'd to ask; but catching the cat, which he knew by feeling, he was observed to look at her steadfastly, and then, setting her down, said, So, puss, I shall know you another time. . . . We thought he soon knew what pictures represented, which were shew'd to him, but we found afterwards we were mistaken; for about two months after he was couch'd, he discovered at once they represented solid bodies, when to that time he considered them only as party-colour'd planes, or surfaces diversified with a variety of paint; . . .

Being shewn his father's picture in a locket in his mother's watch, and told what it was, he acknowledged a likeness, but was vastly surprised; asking, how could it be, that a large face could be express'd in so little room; saying, it should have seemed as impossible to him, as to put a bushel of any thing into a pint. . . .

A year after first seeing, being carried upon Epsom Downs, and observing a large prospect, he was exceedingly delighted with it, and called it a new kind of seeing. And now being lately couch'd of his other eye, he says, that objects at first appeared large to this eye, but not so large as they did at first to the other; and looking upon the same object with both eyes, he thought it looked about twice as large as with the first couch'd eye only, but not double, that we can any ways discover.

B185, B186 Since Cheselden's report, and the other two classical descriptions, by James Ware in 1801 and James Wardrop in 1826, there have been over fifty accounts of the recovery of sight, illustrating the translation of an orientation from an essentially haptic and auditory world into one subservient to the retinal image; and the story is always much the same.

B52 The sixteen best-documented of these case-reports were recently analyzed by C. M. Fisher. Their ages ranged from seven to forty-six, and most of them had had time to enjoy a sufficiently rich and complex perceptual experience relating to the size, shape and significance of objects, as determined by other sensory means. Without exception, they experienced the greatest difficulty in relating the three dimensions they knew from touch to the new two-dimensional image they saw; as in the case of Cheselden's boy, it was months before they were able to accept that the three-dimensional actuality could be amply registered by a two-dimensional picture. Colours were always a problem, for the emotional tones that had previously been developed to give them 'labels' were difficult to adjust to the reality (cf. Locke's blind friend, to whom scarlet signified something 'like the sound of a trumpet'), although the colours could often be registered before the actual forms of the objects they decked, but without having any spatial localization, after the manner of smells.

B103

At first all things were imagined to be touching the eyes, and it was an effort to push them, as it were, back into perspective. In consequence, everything seemed very large, but it was difficult to conceive of objects (such as mountains) being even larger than they actually looked. Vertical and horizontal dimensions were hard to relate. The fields of vision seemed constricted, as the crude image and colours from the peripheral retina were at first too confusing to assess. All the cases had a poor visual memory and a poor capacity for localizing sound.

It was also difficult to relate movements of hand or eye to the newly-seen world: the eyes tended to wander from the object they were trying to inspect, and moved clumsily in the directions to which they were commanded; the pointing finger went awry, and the hands and arms could not indicate the dimensions of familiar objects.

In short, seeing a thing is not an innate and automatic capacity. Every element of what is called 'perception' – line, curve, angle, direction, outline, shape, shadow, form – had to be recognized and acquire meaning. Fisher's conclusion, that perception is not a process separable from recognition, was echoed in the very extensive survey (of 65 cases) by von Senden, who had set out to determine whether the blind from birth have a sense of space, with which a new-found sight can readily be integrated.

B159

It would indeed be interesting to expose such a newly-seeing patient to a truly abstract painting (eschewing representation altogether and dealing entirely with colours – a view which ought to have the qualities of his own natural world), and to encourage him to paint before the interpretation of his colours and shapes begins to sully the 'purity' of his vision.

The personal problems of 'learning to see' are often overwhelming, as the patient may need to shut his eyes again and again, in order to retreat into the security of the sightless world he knows, before resuming the struggle to reassemble his new world, making little or no use of his customary methods of apprehending tactual impressions. His personal life takes on entirely new forms; it is brought home to him how much other people can observe him without laying a hand on him; and he realizes that he must take an interest in his clothes, attend to his hair and watch how other people regard him. He gives up many habits that he could not formerly relinquish, because he is suddenly ashamed of them. He also acquires for the first time an interest in objects and a desire to possess them, that may lead to dissimulation, envy, theft and fraud, and at other times evoke an aesthetic interest that has never been experienced before.

At the end of all this comes the inevitable question – is it really worth it? – when we suggest a sight-restoring operation to a man who, blind from birth, has established for himself a satisfactory orientation and way of life. One recalls the sorry

B70 case of Sidney Bradford, whose corneal opacities (the sequel to infantile vaccination) were grafted away at the age of 52. He found that the transfer from touch to vision proved quite easy, and the minimum of training allowed him to read letters which he had come to know only by touch. Nevertheless, he soon became dispirited; he found the world drab, and was was upset by flaking paint and other blemishes; he liked bright colours, but became depressed when the light faded. And this cheerful, well-adjusted man, with a useful industrial job, who was happily reading Braille in his spare time before the operation, became deeply disturbed thereafter, and, losing his self-respect, soon died in unhappiness. The moral of this story should not be lightly overlooked.

Perhaps I have wandered, in this last chapter, rather far off the road on which we first set forth. For the response to total blindness is many-sided, and involves us in wider issues, to which I could do scant justice. Nevertheless the artistry of the blind, which cannot really be appreciated outside the framework of the blind environment, is at least a crystallization of the world they experience; and of this world the limited visual impediments discussed in the earlier chapters can be held to provide several reflections.

From the diverse interpretations that I have assembled in this book, the reader must accept or reject what he fancies, because by their very nature they can never be wholly established or wholly rejected. In the main they stem from the wave of iconoclasm at the turn of the century; and, once a mechanistic basis for all spiritual and aesthetic experiences has been suggested, all sorts of theories became stuck like burrs on to the accommodating body of this hypothesis, which are naturally suspect in the critical climate of today. But they are none the worse for an airing; for in some of them there are truths that could be worth pursuing.

Notes on the Text

1 Thus R. D. Palmer determined that those with impaired vision were calmer and less excitable, seeking low levels of activation and 'stimulus input'. Stevens and Wolff found that myopic freshmen made significantly better college entrance grades, were more introverted in the thinking and social areas, were more likely to be emotionally inhibited, disinclined to motor-activity and to social leadership, and formed more highly differentiated memory schemata. While Young's more recent analysis of college students showed that whereas the myopes are significantly more orientated towards *abasement* (feeling and accepting guilt), the non-myopes are significantly more given to *exhibition* (wanting to be the centre of attention, talking of their achievements) and to feeling the need for *change* (impatient with the daily routine). Less significantly the myopes rated more highly in *achievement* (the need to do one's best), *intraception* (analyzing one's own and others' feelings), *succorance* (needing help from others when in trouble) and *heterosexuality;* while the non-myopes showed a greater need for *order* and for *dominance* (the need to be leader of the group).

B127

B169

B196

B11

A third analysis of male students by Becker showed that ametropes had higher scores on *application* and *endurance,* but less than the normal-sighted on *achievement.* He also reported the curious finding of a higher proportion of these ametropes among the first-born.

2 Among the central European schools of the period we find the same story, for Oskar Kokoschka, Max Slevogt and Emil Orlik are all recorded as having poor vision; indeed Slevogt 'could not see details at all', and the lack of perspective and depth of the Polish painter Jan Matejko can reasonably be attributed to his myopia, for his spectacles, with -4 D. and -6 D. lenses, have been preserved in the Krakow museum.

Holman Hunt was yet another myope. His spectacles were bequeathed to the museum of the Royal College of Art, but his widow, feeling that myopia was a blemish, apparently went to the length of removing the concave lenses, and inserting weak convex lenses in their place before handing them over.

3 A typical comment is that of *The Times* critic, who described the simplicity and severity of Craig's sets for Ibsen's *The Vikings* as 'harmonious in colouring, broad and massive in design'. Craig himself had later recorded how tremendously a flight of steps appealed to him ('when this desire came to me, I was continually designing dramas, wherein the place was architectural, and lent itself to my desire').

B97

His biographer also describes how 'in the early days, when Craig was young and unknown, among the few who understood his aim had been the poet W. B. Yeats . . . who would discourse on the poetic drama in his vivid magnetic way, peering with myopic eyes into the darkness while Craig was happy to sit and listen to him.' It is tempting to suggest that the vision he so readily shared with Yeats was really a sharing of their mutual dependence on the strange structural world of the myope which Mills so compellingly described (see p. 32).

4 These convex mirrors were used in all seriousness by the Dutch naturalistic artists of the previous century, sometimes in the form

B189

of a crystal ball which is actually depicted in certain of their studies, and this in turn probably derives from their use of one or more mirrors (typically by Vermeer) – a method said to originate with Titian's exploitation of Venetian glass. Gerard Dou is said to have manipulated with his foot a screen in which was set a concave lens bearing a grid of threads to correspond with a similar grid on his canvas.

5 Of the molluscs, even the cephalopods (octopi and cuttlefish), with their highly-developed eyes and excellent form-discrimination, seem to have no true colour sense. Among arthropods, the

higher crustaceans (such as the lobster) have well-organized eyes comparable to those of their insect cousins, but little sign of colour discrimination, perhaps because they are largely nocturnal in habit; and even the insects are primarily orientated by smell. Although colour-vision varies in different insect species, they generally have a higher response to wave-length changes in the blue to ultraviolet range, and, after that, in the red-yellow range; insects also have a unique visual capacity of appreciating changes in the polarization of light.

6 The lowest primates are essentially colour-blind. The new-world monkeys have a deficient red-green discrimination comparable to that of colour-blind humans, whereas the old-world monkeys have the normal human colour values.   B178

7 H. Osborne summarizes the colour concepts of the ancient Greeks thus. They were not given to careful discrimination of colour hue,   B125 and there is little evidence of attention to hues except possibly within the violet-purple band. The Greek colour-vocabulary was jejune, and the available terms were bunched into a small number of groups. Within each group the terms did not differentiate in virtue of hue, but were used indifferently as synonyms or differentiated in respect of brightness and intensity. In their literature the Greeks used words signifying black, white, grey, green, blue-purple, yellow-orange and red, each with a number of alternative names that probably relate to different degrees of brightness; indeed in the dramas there are only the most elementary references to colour, and then usually referring to brightness rather than hue. From their specific writings on colour, black, white, red and light green were regarded as the primaries by Democritus, while Aristotle thought that the rainbow had only three essential colours – red, green and blue.

In their paintings the ancient Greeks traditionally used only three colours (black, white and red), to which yellow was later added (according to Roman writers, by Polygnotus between 475 and 440 BC), but many other pigments and dyes were in fact available and used. They were far more concerned with saturation and brightness than with hue, and it is probable that fairly violent colours were used lavishly, and without much reference to naturalism, on most of the statuary, but no original paintings of the great period (fifth and fourth century BC) have survived, and it was not until the Augustan period that moderation in the use of colours was achieved.

The common practice of relating specific colour names to specific subjects rather than hues (green-eyed Athene, rosy-fingered dawn, etc.) has continued down to the present in many languages (like Swahili) that are off the main stream of civilization.

B44   8 Dorn has described a unique patient who could selectively respond
         to differing X-ray waves, invisible to the normal eye.
       9 Such as: the crocean and amethystine lustre; amaranthine weed;
         greening-sapphire sea; rubied sun; ruby-plumaged flames;
         pearled moon; a ribbed track of cloudy malachite; clarified silver;
         golden bars (golden and silvery appear very often); metallic
         vapours; burnished sun.
      10 'Voyelles' – Rimbaud – (from *Premiers Vers*):

> *A noir, E blanc, I rouge, U vert, O bleu: voyelles,*
> *Je dirai quelque jour vos naissances latentes:*
> *A, noir corset velu des mouches éclatantes*
> *Qui bombinent autour des puanteurs cruelles,*
>
> *Golfes d'ombre; E, candeurs des vapeurs et des tentes,*
> *Lances des glaciers fiers, rois blancs, frissons d'ombelles;*
> *I, pourpres, sang craché, rire des lèvres belles*
> *Dans la colère ou les ivresses pénitentes;*
>
> *U, cycles, vibrements divins des mers virides,*
> *Paix des pâtis semés d'animaux, paix des rides*
> *Que l'alchimie imprime aux grands fronts studieux;*
>
> *O, suprême Clairon plein de strideurs étranges,*
> *Silences traversés des Mondes et des Anges:*
> *– O l'Oméga, rayon violet de Ses Yeux!*

      11 Of her long vowels, a = pink, e = rust, i = white, o = blue,
         u = dark green.
         Of her musical notes, A = peach, C = orange/gray, D = blue/
         green, F = yellow, G = red.
      12 Purple – 'the colour of amethysts, pageantry, royalty and death',
         Red   – 'the colour of rubies, wine, revelry, furnaces, courage
                  and magic',
         Blue – 'the colour of sapphires, deep water, skies, loyalty and
                  melancholy',
         Green – 'the colour of emeralds, hope, youth, joy, spring and
                  victory'.
      13 A 'Really excellent' treatment for cataract entails the insertion of
         malachite, pounded with honey, while incanting: 'Come
         Malachite, Come Thou Green one. Come discharge from Horus'
         eye. Come Secretion from Atun's eye...'
            Since all colours had, to early civilizations, a supernatural
B49   quality, the Ebers Papyrus contains a host of other such formulas,
         recommended because of the colour of their ingredients.
      14 'The sun, too, blinds, ... because his power is great, and the idols

from him are borne through the clear air, sinking heavily into the deep, and strike upon the eyes, disordering their texture.'

15 Several other instances of colour-defective artists have been described and analyzed. The following account is included, since it is presented from the slightly different standpoint of a young art-teacher.

One of the students, an extremely quiet and sensitive boy, was about 17 when he joined my composition class. The first painting he produced, a street scene, showed a fair sense of arrangement, good drawing, and very unusual colour for a beginner. He used colours which were bright but not crude, with some red and yellow, a little green, and a great deal of soft blue and mauve. The general effect was exciting and pleasing; a change from the usual red, yellow, blue and viridian in their raw state used by most beginners.

During the following lesson a week later, he asked if he could speak to me privately, and he then told me that he was completely colour-blind. He said that he knew which colours to use by the names on the tubes of paint, and that his difficulty lay in the painting of shadows. Evidently he knew, or had been told, that there was colour in shadows, but in trying to paint a cool shadow on a warm-coloured object he could not judge the quantity of the cool pigment he was adding, and often changed the original colour completely. When I saw his painting again this was obvious: a red object, for example, might be shaded in blue or purple; the colour change being so violent that the object was split completely. Although the colour values were wrong the tone values were so good that they gave the picture a unity which it would otherwise have completely lacked. All the objects in the composition, as far as I can remember, were painted in their correct colours, blue sky, red roofs, &c.

A colleague tells me that when painting from still life the student later developed a method of working which made up for his colour-blindness. Although the objects he was painting were in front of him (in my class, students worked from memory) he never actually made a mistake in identifying the colour of an object, nor did he ever ask the master to tell him. He may, however, have asked other students. His colour in this class was extremely subdued, quiet and 'safe'; there was nothing wrong with it but its extreme dullness. The form and tone were very good. He had obviously worked out a formula for colour which compensated for whatever defect he had, but which was extremely narrow and incapable of being developed.

He eventually took up sculpture but I don't believe his work was outstanding.

16 This change can be assessed by matching graded colours on a Davidson and Hemmendiger colour-rule.

B109

17 *Minerva flavo lumine est: Venus paeto.*
'Auctor Priapeorum' 37 (Aurelius Augustinius), AD 51.
[Minerva has golden eyes, Venus a cast.]
Non haec res de Venere paeta strabam fecit?
'Priscianus' (M. Terentius Varro). *c.* AD 500.
[Did not this confer a squint on cast-eyed Venus?]
Si Paeta est, Veneri similis.
'Ars Amatoria' 2/659, Ovidius Naso, 45 BC–AD 17.
[If she has a cast, she is like Venus.]

18 This dominance of the right field (to the right-handed) evidently depends on the underlying hemi-cerebral dominance and is not in fact a sequel to the directional scanning, since it is most evident with the use of identifiable symbols (and field dominance is least evident when we contrast 'nonsense shapes' or geometrical forms); and it is less selective in the left-handed. Field dominance becomes less strong where the eye-dominance is greatest, suggesting that eye-dominance is a manifestation of highly differentiated functioning, and where this is well-developed, the subject can become relatively field-independent.

B21

B124

B14

19 They may also suffer from word-blindness ('dyslexia'), and are prone to Spoonerisms. There is a well-established relationship between speech difficulties and left-hand dominance, especially when the subject is forced to use his right hand; and symptoms related to eye-hand confusion mainly follow if the controlling eye is on the opposite side to the 'handedness' of the subject. But the picture is further confused in that the dominant eye, the sighting eye and the chief eye from a monocular standpoint, is not always the controlling eye when the two eyes are working as a team.

B16

20   Thee I revisit safe;
And feel thy sov'reign vital lamp; but thou
Revisit'st not these eyes, that roll in vain
To find thy piercing ray, and find no dawn;
So thick a drop serene hath quench'd their orbs,
Or dim suffusion veil'd.
                              Paradise Lost, III

21 There is always a temptation to overstretch one's medical analogies. It has not always been easy to resist seeking points in common between the work of two sufferers of an identical disorder, and then attribute this common feature to the malady in question. But Wyndham Lewis, with his brilliantly coloured paintings and his

vorticist prose, could hardly be more alien from Milton, with his colour-images that were so sparse and sombre, and with the 'organ-voiced' grandeur of his epic style.

22 His brain, with its tumour, is preserved in the Pathological Museum at Westminster Hospital.

23 The fully-sighted are normally spared these intrusions, at least when the eyes are open; but one author (A.W.) has described how, for over two years, he was constantly being disturbed by the portrait of his mother, who had died in his childhood, appearing whenever he closed his eyes; and another (P.W.) was beset by bizarre little figures that made him dread the time for sleep. In Germany this apparently clear vision through closed eyes has been labelled the 'Tiberius phenomenon'. It was noted in patients whose eyes were bandaged, or even removed; and some even claimed clear 'visual' images through the back of their heads.

24 Adjacent to this 'occipital' area of the brain, on which the visual images are reproduced, and then 'perceived' by the mind, lies a 'parietal' area in which such percepts are coordinated and rationalized; and several patients have been reported in whom injuries or tumours of this area may so upset the visual feedback that they can only draw or paint while both eyes are kept closed. B42

25 The alternative theory of Euclid and Ptolemy had it that the 'rays' went in the reverse direction – outwards from the eye – but the eye still remained the avenue of contact. By the Renaissance, the correct view (the older Epicurean 'Intromission' theory) was winning; and Leonardo accepted the old emanation theory only 'when considering the beguiling power of a maiden's eye'. Even B88 so, the emanation theory has continued as the basis of the belief in the Evil Eye right up to the present; and less than fifty years ago a reputable London doctor described in *The Lancet* 'an instrument set in motion by vision'. B150

26 The pineal body still functions as a third eye among certain reptiles. In mammals its functions are obscure, but it does contain a chemical that helps the cerebral function and which is specifically disrupted by LSD. The pineal body's function can be affected by changing light conditions and it has been suggested that the religious festivals of the ancients, grouped around equinoxes and solstices, were thus arranged when stimulation of this 'third eye' made ecstatic experiences more accessible.

27 On this replacement basis, the Persian Shah, Aga Mohammed, who had been castrated, took his revenge on society by ordering 30,000 human eyes to be brought to him, which he then counted himself. This ocular projection of sexuality is largely a masculine outlet, since it is the male who traditionally makes the selection of his sexual partner, and is guided in this by the woman's appear-

ance, whereas the woman, traditionally a passive recipient of such attentions, has less occasion to bother about the appearance of the male. And it is the male who principally elaborates his visual fantasies as a sex incentive or substitute (hence the scotophilia, for the actual woman rarely lives up to the appearance of the fantasy one), whereas the female is primarily exhibitionistic and non-cerebral in her sex.

28 The English, with their nonconformist consciences, and in contrast to the Latins, are said to be largely scotophiliac, preferring their intercourse in the darkness. One recalls the curious finding that a quarter of the women attending a provincial hospital, when questioned whether their husbands were circumcised or not, did not know the answer as they had never seen them naked.

29 J. M. Heaton describes one psychopath who travelled for her analysis only at dusk with veil, goggles and heavy-brimmed hat, and others who identified the sun and its light with their fellow's watchful eye, detecting their incestuous wishes.

B73

30 The hysterical belief in the damaging effects of sexual incontinence a century ago is as incomprehensible now as the equivalent fear of witchcraft in the centuries that went before. Insanity and blindness headed the list, which culminated in a 14-page article in the reputable *Archives of Ophthalmology* of 1882 entitled 'Eye Diseases and Masturbation'. Six years later the presidential address to the Ophthalmological Society of the United Kingdom explains at length how masturbation can produce amblyopia, retinal haemorrhage, follicular inflammation, catarrh, trachoma, retinal irritation, neuro-retinitis (in young ladies) and total blindness, not to mention agoraphobia and other more bizarre sequelae. And even in 1964 we still find a Professor of Ophthalmology citing as the nine causes of defective eyesight an 'excess of sexual appetite'!

B33

B139

B8

31 Roger Bacon (1214–99) tells how Alexander the Great once attacked a city defended by a basilisk on its walls; advised by Aristotle, he used a large polished surface to reflect the poisonous glance and destroy the serpent. But to most authorities, even the mirror could reflect the damaging rays. Sir Thomas Browne believed that Evil Eyes could even transmit infections when reflected from a mirror; and authorities such as Pliny, St Thomas Aquinas and Roger Bacon knew that the mirror was always dulled by such a glance – a diagnostic test that was freely used to expose witches and criminals.

32 Milton, indeed, believed that his own insight was increased by his loss of vision, and Dr Pierre Villey, himself blind, writes:

'There is more equilibrium and judgment with the gifted blind man than with the man who can see. This is not surprising, for

B182

sight is the sense for amusement. The less one is disturbed thus, the less one's inner thoughts are interrupted by outward events, the more one is concentrated on oneself, the more time one takes to ripen one's reflections, and to weigh the for-and-against of one's deliberations.'

James Thurber, who lost the sight of both eyes through retinal detachments, said:

'A blind man benefits by lack of distractions; my one-eighth vision happily obscures sad and ungainly sights, leaving only the vivid and the radiant, some of whom are my friends and neighbours.'

33 As J. F. Wilson put it: 'Hayes' theory of the vicariate of the senses could not survive the statistics of Greisbach and Kunz who, after measuring the sensory acuity of a respectable number of blind children in France and Germany, concluded that the loss of a major sense impairs rather than increases the acuity of the others.' B192

A more recent survey by Ewart, who tested the tactile recognition of form in 30 blind and 30 sighted children, showed no significant difference except when the children had a high I.Q., in which case they were materially more successful than their sighted colleagues. B50

34 The formal explanation of Rosa's cutaneous photo-sensitivity was that it was associated with the ability of nerve-endings in her skin to record chemical changes from light in the form of a mosaic, for it was found that this sensitivity could be lowered by careful washing and extraction of the carotenoids from her stratum corneum. American investigators have postulated other pigments, possibly enhanced by melanin, differential penetration of differing wave-lengths, and so on. None of these carries great conviction. B111, 167

35 Both Bach and Handel had their cataracts removed by the arch-charlatan Chevalier Taylor, surgeon-oculist to the Princess of Wales, who failed to restore sight in either of them. That was in the years 1750–51, eight years after Daviel had introduced a technique for properly removing the cataract, which Taylor never mastered. In fact both were probably blind from another cause. As well as being clinically irresponsible, Taylor's accounts, such as his assertion that he also de-cataracted Edward Gibbon, cannot be trusted. B154

36 An exception to this was John Stanley, the distinguished composer and organist who was blinded in infancy. It was once suggested that he might collaborate with his contemporary, Handel, when the latter was grieving that blindness had robbed him of any power to compose.

Bibliography

1 AHLENSTIEL, Heinz (1952) – 'On light-less and eye-less sight'. *Klin. Mbl. Augenheilk., 121, 92.*

2 AHLSTRÖM, O. (1955) – 'The Eyesight of Some Renaissance Artists'. *Opt. Sci. Instr. Mkr., 130, 253.*

3 ALAERTS, Louis (1958) – *La Myopie Héréditaire des Medicis.* Laboratoires Cusi, Brussels.

4 AMES, A., PROCTOR, C. A., and AMES, B. (1923) – 'Vision and the Technique of Art'. *Proc. Amer. Acad. Arts and Sciences, 58, 1.*

5 ANGELUCCI, A. (1908) – 'Les Peintures des Daltoniens'. *Rec. d'Ophtal.* (Paris), *30, 1.*

6 ANTROBUS, J. S., DEMENT, W., FISHER, C. (1964) – 'Eye movements accompanying day dreaming, visual imagery, and thought suppression'. *J. Abnorm. Soc. Psychol.,* 69, 244.

7 ARDIZZONE, Edward (1963) – Personal communication.

8 AGARWAL, K. M. (1964) – 'The Cause of defective eyesight and fundamental principles of normal sight'. *Med. Digest* (Bombay), *32, 471.*

9 BARSLEY, M. (1966) – *The Left-handed Book.* Souvenir Press, London.

10 BEATTIE, P. H. (1953) – 'The Ocular Troubles of Dr Johnson and Mr Pepys'. *Proc. Roy. Soc. Med., 46, 591.*

11 BECKER, G. (1965) – 'Visual Acuity, Birth order, Achievement versus Affiliation, and other Edwards Personal Preference Schedule Scores'. *J. Psychom. Res., 9, 277.*

12 BEDE, Venerable (*c.* AD 720) – *De Natura Rerum.*

13 BELL, J. (1926) – *Treasury of Human Intelligence,* Vol. II, Cambridge.

14 BELMONT, L., BIRCH, H. G. (1965) – 'Lateral Dominance, Lateral Awareness and Reading Disability'. *Child Develop., 36, 57.*

15 BERKELEY, George, Bishop of Cloyne (1709) – *Essay Towards a New Theory of Vision.* Printed by Aaron Rhames for Jeremy Pepyat, Dublin.

16 BERNER, G. E. and BERNER, B. S. (1953) – 'Relation of Ocular dominance, handedness, and the controlling eye in binocular vision'. *A.M.A. Arch. Ophthal., 50, 603.*

17 BLUM, H. (1964) – 'Colour in Dreams'. *Internat. J. Psychoanal.*, *45*, 519.

18 BOZZOLI, S. (1957) – *Otium (L'Occhio del mio Amico Poeta)*. Treviso.

19 BROSCHMANN, D. (1966) – 'Der Farbenuntüchtige und seine Umwelt'. *Klin. Mbl. Augenheilk.*, *148*, Bd. 2, 290.

20 BROWN, E. G. (1934) – *Milton's Blindness*. Columbia Univ. Press, New York.

21 BRYDEN, M. P. (1966) – 'Left-right differences in tachistoscopic recognitions'. *Percept. Motor Skills*, *23*, 1127.

22 CANTAMESSA, G. (1938) – 'Occhio e Pittura'. *Boll. Oculist.*, *17*, 1035.

23 CARSTAIRS, Morris (1966) – 'The Madness of Art'. *Observer* (Col. Supp.), 12 October.

24 CAWTHORNE, Terence (1959) – 'The last illness of Oscar Wilde'. *Proc. Roy. Soc. Med.*, *52*, 1.

25 CAWTHORNE, Terence (1960) – 'The influence of deafness on the creative instinct'. *Laryngoscope*, *70*, 1110.

26 CAWTHORNE, Terence (1962) – 'Goya's illness'. *Proc. Roy. Soc. Med.*, *55*, 213.

27 CERBUS, G., NICHOLS, R. C. (1963) – 'Personality Variables and response to colour'. *Psychol. Bull.*, *60*, 566.

28 CHANCE, Burton (1939) – 'Sir Joshua Reynolds and his blindness and death'. *Ann. med. hist.*, *3*, 487.

29 CHANCE, Burton (1962) – *Clio Medica-Ophthalmology*, Hafner Publ. Co., New York, p. 124.

30 CHESELDEN, Wm. (1728) – 'An account of Observations made by a young gentleman . . .'. *Philosoph. Trans.* (April–June), 7–402, 447.

31 CHILD, I. L. (1965) – 'Personality Correlates of Aesthetic Judgement in College Students'. *J. Personality.*, *33*, 476.

32 COATES, W. H. (1939) – *Beating Shoes,* Heath Cranston Ltd, London.

33 COHN, Hermann (1882) – 'Eye Diseases and Masturbation'. *Arch. Ophthal.*

34 COLQUHOUN, N. C., and PALMER, H. (1953) – 'Pictorial art, viewed from the standpoint of mental organisation as revealed by the excitatory abreactive techniques of psychiatry'. *J. Mental Sci.*, *99*, 136.

35 CRITCHLEY, MacDonald (1928) – *Mirror Writing*. Psyche Miniatures No. 11, Kegan Paul, Trench, Trubner & Co., London.

36 CROFT-MURRAY, E. (1959) – *Decorative Painting In England*, 1537–1837. Country Life Ltd, London.

37 DESNEUX, Jules (1951) – *Rigueur de Jan van Eyck*. Editions des Artistes, Brussels.

38 DEVEREUX, G. (1967) – 'Observations and belief in Aischylos' account of dreams'. *Psychother, Psychosom., 15,* 114.

39 DOBRONRAVOV, S. N., FISHELEV, Y. R. – 'Cutaneous Vision'. *Fed. Proc. Transl. Supp., 29,* 659.

40 DOESSCHATE, G. Ten (1946) – 'Some historical notes on Spectacles and on Beryllus'. *Brit. J. Ophthal., 30,* 660.

41 DOGGART, James H. (1963) – 'Gibbon's Eyesight'. *Trans. Cambridge Biblio. Soc., 3,* No. 5, 406.

42 DONGEN, H. R., Van FORTUYN, J. D. (1968) – 'Drawing with closed eyes'. *Psychiat. Neurol. Neuro-Chir., 71,* 275.

43 DONNET, L. (1963) – 'Couleurs et Temperaments'. *Presse med., 71,* 2008.

44 DORN, E. (1903) – 'Ueber die Sichtbarkeit der Röntgenstrahlen für vollständig Farbenblinde'. *Wiedem. Ann. Phys. Chem., 68,* 1171.

45 DOUGLAS, J. W. B., ROSS, J. M. and SIMPSON, H. R. (1967) – 'The ability and attainment of short-sighted pupils'. *J. Roy. Stat. Soc.,* Vol. *130,* Series A, 479.

46 DOUGLAS, J. W. B., ROSS, J. M., and SIMPSON, H. R. (1968) – *All Our Future.* Peter Davies Ltd, London.

47 DOUGLAS, W. O. (1950) – *Strange Lands and Friendly People.* Harper, New York.

48 DREWRY, Yvonne (1968) – Report in *East Anglian Daily Times,* 8 May.

49 EBERS PAPYRUS, THE (*c.* 1550 BC) – Trans. by Ebbell, Levin and Munksgaard, Copenhagen, 1937, p. 73.

50 EWART, A. G., CARP, F. M. (1963) – 'Recognition of tactual forms by sighted and blind subjects'. *Amer. J. Psychol., 76,* 488.

51 FABRICANT, Noah D. (1957) – 'The Ocular History of James Joyce'. *EENT Monthly, 36,* 731.

52 FISHER, C. M. (1964) – 'The later acquisition of vision by persons born blind'. *Trans. Amer. Neurol. Ass., 89,* 195.

53 FISHER, S. (1965) – 'Sex Designations of right and left body-sides and assumptions about male-female superiority'. *J. Personality Soc. Psychol. 2,* 576.

54 FOSTER, John (1953) – 'Curiosa Ophthalmica'. *Trans. ophthal. soc. Australia, 12,* 28.

55 FOULKES, D., PIVIK, T., STEADMAN, H. S., SPEAR, P. S., SYMONDS, J. D. (1967) – 'Dreams of the male child'. *J. Abnorm. Psychol. 72,* 457.

56 FRANCESCHETTI, A. (1939) – 'Sur le rapport entre phosphènes mécaniques provoqués et certaines affections oculaires'. (*Congr. Soc. franc. ONO Bordeaux,* 3 June 38). *Cité Rev. ONO, 17,* 244.

57 FRENCH, C. N. (1965) – 'Tactile Vision, Thermal and Texture cues in the discrimination of black and white'. *Nature* (London), *208,* 1352.

58 FRY, Sara Margery (1954) – *Old Age Looks at Itself.* National Old People's Welfare Council, London, p. 4. Reprinted from 'Old Age in the Modern World'. *Report of the third Congress of Int. Assn. of Gerontology,* London.

59 GAIRDNER, D. (1949) – 'The Fate of the Foreskin: A study of circumcision'. *Brit. med. J., 2,* 1433.

60 GALTON, Francis (1883) – *Inquiries into Human Faculty.* Macmillan, London, p. 47.

61 GALVAO, P. G. (1964) – 'Hypertelorism and Divergent Strabismus in the work of Aleijedinho'. *Rev. Brasil. Oftal., 23,* 265.

62 GARDNER, Martin (1967) – *The Ambidextrous Universe.* Allen Lane, The Penguin Press, London.

63 GARMA, A. (1961) – 'Colour in Dreams'. *Int. J. Psychoanal. 42,* 556

64 GASSON, W. (1969) – 'The Florentine Legend'. *Ophthalmic Optician,* 6 Sept., p. 124.

65 GIFFORD, Edward S. (1958) – *The Evil Eye.* Macmillan Co., New York.

66 GLADSTONE, Wm. Ewart (1858) – *Homer and the Homeric Age,* London.

67 GOODENOUGH, D. R., LEWIS, H. B., SHAPIRO, A., JARET, L., SLESER, I. (1965) – 'Dream reporting'. *J. Personality Soc. Psychol. 2,* 170.

68 GORMAN, H. (1948) – *James Joyce.* Rinehart & Co., New York.

69 GRAVES, Robert (1955) – *The Greek Myths.* Penguin Books Ltd, Harmondsworth, England, p. 37.

70 GREGORY, R. L. and WALLACE, J. G. (1963) – Recovery From Early Blindness. EPS Monograph, No. 2, Cambridge.

71 HARDY, W. E. (1934) – *Random Reflections on Ophthalmo-Optical History, Techniques, Philosophy, Literature and Personalities.* Hatton Press, London.

72 HAYASHI, T. and BRYDEN, M. P. (1967) – 'Ocular Dominance and Perceptual asymmetry'. *Percept. Motor Skills, 25,* 605.

73 HEATON, J. M. (1968) – *The Eye, Phenomenology and Psychology of Function and Disorder.* Tavistock, Lippincott, London.

74 HOWARD, J. R. (1954) – *Guildcraft* (June), p. 21.

75 HUBER, O. (1932) – 'Zu Grecos Astigmatismus'. *Klin. Mbl. Augenheilk., 89,* 97.

76 HUBER, O. (1935) – 'Auf meines Publikation "Zu Greco's Astigmatismus" '. *Z. Augenheilk., 86,* 37.

77 HUBER, O. (1935) – 'Vergleichende Augenheilkunde'. *Klin. Mbl. Augenheilk., 95,* 574.

78 HUXLEY, Aldous (1954) – *The Doors of Perception.* Penguin Books Ltd, Harmondsworth, England, p. 19.

79 INMAN, W. S. (1939) – 'The Symbolic significance of glass in relation to diseases of the eye'. *Brit. J. Psychol., 18,* 122.

80 INMAN, W. S. (1946) – 'Styes, barley and wedding rings'. *Brit. J. med. Psychol., 70, 331.*

81 INMAN, W. S. (1965) – 'Emotional factors in corneal disease'. *Brit. J. med. Psychol., 38, 277.*

82 'INSIGHT' (Editorial pub. by Portland Publications, 91–101, Oxford Press for the publisher Smith, Miller and Patch, Inc., N.Y.) Nov.–Dec. 1967, p. 3.

83 ISAKOWITZ, J. (1918) – 'Zur Frage der Beziehungen zwischen Refraktion und dem Werk des Malers'. *Klin. Mbl. Augenheilk., 61, 454.*

84 ISAKOWITZ, J. (1933) – 'Zu Grecos Astigmatismus'. (Eine Replik). *Klin. Mbl. Augenheilk., 91, 110.*

85 JACKSON, D. M. (1968) – 'Bach, Handel and the Chevalier Taylor'. *Med. Hist., 12, 385.*

86 JAMES, William (1890) – *The Principles of Psychology.* New York, vol. 2, p. 84.

87 KARACAN, I., GOODENOUGH, D. R., SHAPIRO, A., STARKER, S. (1966) – 'Erection cycle during sleep in relation to dream anxiety'. *Arch. Gen. Psychiat.* (Chicago), *15, 183.*

88 KEELE, K. D. (1955) – 'Leonardo da Vinci on Vision'. *Proc. Roy. Soc. Med., 48, 384.*

89 KELLOG, Rhoda, KNOLL, M. and KUGLER, J. (1965) – 'Form-similarity between phosphenes of adults and pre-school children's scribblings'. *Nature, 208,* 1129.

90 KRAHMER, W. and KORST, L. (1925) – 'Zum Problem der Links und Rechtshandigkeit'. *J. für Psychol. u. Neurol., 31,* 311.

91 LAKOWSKI, R. and MONTGOMERY, G. W. G. (1968) – 'Colour Discrimination in profoundly deaf children'. Paper presented at 2nd Scottish Symposium on Colour, 6 Sept.

92 LANG, S. (1968) – 'Colour preferences in choosing towels'. *Proc. II Scottish Symposium on Colour,* Edinburgh.

93 LARSSON, S. (1965) – *Konstnärens Öga.* Stockholm.

94 LAW, B. M. (1957) – 'Constable and Colour'. Paper read during Cdn. Ophthal. Cong. at Banff, Alberta.

95 LAWLER, C. D., LAWLER, E. E. (1965) – 'Colour-mood associations in young children'. *J. Genet. Psychol., 107, 29.*

96 LEBER, T. (1877) – 'Die angeborene Amaurose durch Retinal-atrophie'. *Graefe-Saemisch Handb. g. Augenheilk.,* I, *5,* 648.

97 LEEPER, Janet (1948) – *Edward Gordon Craig.* Penguin Books Ltd, Harmondsworth, England.

98 LE GRAND, Y. (1952) – *Optique Physiologie.* Revue d'Optique, Paris.

99 LEWIN, B. D. (1946) – 'Sleep, the mouth and the dream screen'. *Psychoanal. Quart., 15,* 419.

100 LEWIS, W. (1951) – *The Listener,* 10 May.

101 LIEBREICH, R. (1872) – 'Turner and Mulready – On the Effect of certain Faults of Vision on Painting, with especial reference to their Works'. *Not. Proc. Roy. Inst.*, *6*, 450.

102 LINKSZ, A. (1965) – 'An ophthalmologist looks at art and artists'. *Proc. Amer-Hungarian Med. Ass.*, *1*, 1.

103 LOCKE, John (1690) – *Essay Concerning Human Understanding*.

104 LOWENFELD, V. (1939) – *The Nature of Creative Artistry*. Routledge and Kegan Paul, London.

105 LOWENFELD, V. (1951) – 'Psycho-aesthetic Implications of the Art of the blind'. *J. Aesthetics and Art Criticism*, *10*, 1.

106 LUCRETIUS (*c.* 60 BC) – *De Rerum Natura*. Book 4, p. 325. Trans. Bailey (1921), Clarendon Press, Oxford.

107 LURIA, A. R. (1938) – *The Mind of a Mnemonist*. Jonathan Cape, London.

108 MACHOTKA, P. (1966) – 'Aesthetic Preferences in Childhood: Justification of Preferences'. *Child Develop.*, *37*, 877.

109 MACLAREN, K. (1969) – *Corres. J. Soc. Dyerists and Colourists*, *85*, 31.

110 MAJEWSKI, K. A. (1936) – 'Sur la myopie de Jean Matejko, Peintre polonais'. *Ann. Oculist.* (Paris), *173*, 554.

111 MAKOUS, W. L. (1966) – 'Cutaneous Colour Sensitivity'. *Psychol. Review*, *73*, 292.

112 MARQUEZ, M. (1926) – 'Sobre el Supuesto Astigmatismo del Greco'. *Arch. Oftal. hisp.-amer.*, *26*, 715.

113 MARQUEZ, M. (1929) – 'El mundo exterior, la imagen retiniana y la función visual. Con motivo del pretendido astigmatismo del Greco'. *Rev. españ. de med. y. cir.*, *12*, 264.

114 MARSHALL, A. J. (1954) – *Bower Birds*. Oxford University Press.

115 MILES, W. E. (1954) – 'How colours affect us'. *Today's Health*, No. 24. Quoted by Schlaeger, T. F. (1957) – *Psychometric Ophthalmology*. Williams and Williams Co., Baltimore.

116 MILLER, S. (1964) – 'The manifest dream and the appearance of colour in Dreams'. *Int. J. Psychoanal.*, *45*, 512.

117 MILLS, L. (1936) – 'Peripheral Vision in Art'. *Arch. Ophthal.* (Chicago), *16*, 208.

118 MORRIS, D. (1960) – *The Biology of Art*. Methuen, London, p. 22.

119 MULLER, K. (1961) – 'Beethovens Brille'. *Klin. Mbl. Augen-heilk.*, *138*, 412.

120 MULLER, K. (1961) – 'Goethes Augengläser'. *Klin. Mbl. Augenheilk.*, *138*, 882.

121 MULLER, K. (1964) – 'The Eyeglasses of Famous Men'. *Klin. Mbl. Augenheilk.*, *145*, 124.

122 NAITO, Y. (1966) – 'A theory for development of Myopia – Emotion and myopia'. *Folia. Ophthal. Jap.*, *17*, 1131.

123 NORTHCOTE, J. (1818) – *Life of Sir Joshua Reynolds.* 2nd ed. Henry Colburn, London, p. 246.
124 OLTMAN, P. K., CAPOBIANCO, F. (1967) – 'Field dependence and eye dominance'. *Percept. Motor Skills, 25,* 645.
125 OSBORNE, H. (1968) – 'Colour Concepts of the Ancient Greeks'. *Brit. J. Aesthetics, 8,* 269.
126 OSTWALD, P. F. (1964) – 'Colour hearing: A missing link between normal perception and the hallucination'. *Arch. Gen. Psychiat.* (Chicago), *11,* 40.
127 PALMER, R. D. (1966) – 'Visual Acuity and Excitement'. *Psychosom. med., 28,* 364.
128 PATRY, A. (1917) – 'Welchen Einfluss hat die Refraktion auf das Werk des Malers'. *Klin. Mbl. Augenheilk., 58,* 597.
129 PEARSON, K. (1924) – *The Life of Francis Galton.* Vol. II, Cambridge.
130 PICK, H. L. (1964) – 'Perception in Soviet Psychology'. *Psycholog. Bulletin, 62,* 21.
131 PICKFORD, R. W. (1957) – *Individual Differences in Colour Vision.* Routledge and Kegan Paul, London.
132 PICKFORD, R. W. (1964) – 'A Deuteranomalous artist'. *Brit. J. Psychol., 55,* 469.
133 PICKFORD, R. W. (1965) – 'Two Artists with Protanope Colour Vision Defects'. *Brit. J. Psychol., 56,* 421.
134 PICKFORD, R. W. (1967) – 'Colour-defective students in Colleges of Art'. *Brit. J. Aesth., 7, 132.*
135 PICKFORD, R. W. and TAYLOR, W. O. G. (1968) – 'Colour vision of two Albinos'. *Brit. J. Ophthal., 52,* No. 8, 640.
136 PLESCH, John (1947) – *Janós, the Story of a Doctor.* London.
137 POST, R. H. (1962) – 'Population differences in red and green colour vision deficiency'. *Eugenics Quarterly, 9,* No. 1, 181.
138 POST, R. H. (1962) – 'Population differences in vision acuity'. *Eugenics Quarterly, 9,* No. 4, 189.
139 POWER, Henry (1888) – 'Relation of Ophthalmic Disease to certain normal and psychological conditions of the sexual organs'. *Trans. Ophthal. Soc. UK, 7,* 1.
140 RÉVÉSZ, G. (1950) – *Psychology and Art of the Blind.* Transl. by H. Wolff, Longmans Green, London.
141 RICE, T. (1930) – 'Physical defects in Character, I, Farsightedness'. *Hygeia, 8,* 536.
142 RICE, T. (1930) – 'Physical defects in Character, II, Nearsightedness'. *Hygeia, 8,* 644.
143 RICKERS-OVSIANKINA, M. A., KNAPP, R. H., MCINTYRE, D. W. (1963) – 'Factors affecting the psychodiagnostic significance of colour perception'. *J. Project. Techn., 27,* 461.
144 RIDDELL, W. J. B. (1949) – 'Discussion on colour vision in industry'. *Proc. Roy. Soc. Med., 42,* 145.

145 RIDLEY, F. (1952) – 'Some reflections on visual perception'. *Trans. Ophthal. Soc. UK, 72, 635.*

146 RILKE, R. M. (1917) – *Rodin, the Man and His Art.* New York.

147 ROCK, I., HARRIS, C. S. (1967) – 'Vision and Touch'. *Sci. American, 216, 96.*

148 ROGERS-LAMBERT (1949) – 'John Milton's Blindness: a suggested diagnosis'. *J. Hist. Med., 4, 468.*

149 ROSS, B. M. (1966) – 'Minimal Familiarity and Left–Right Judgement of Paintings'. *Percept. Motor Skills, 22, 105.*

150 RUSS, Charles (1921) – 'An Instrument set in motion by vision or by the proximity of the human body'. *The Lancet, ii, 222.*

151 SAJNER, J. (1965) – 'Gregor Johann Mendel's vision and eyeglasses'. *Klin. Mbl. Augenheilk., 147, 600.*

152 SAMUEL, Edgar (1963) – 'Death in the glass – a new view of Holbein's Ambassadors'. *The Burlington Magazine,* Vol. 105, Oct. 1963, p. 436.

153 SAVIN, L. (1958) – 'Influence of vascular changes in progressive failure of vision'. *Trans. Ophthal. Soc. UK, 78, 315.*

154 SCARLETT, E. P. (1964) – 'A Doctor comments on Bach'. *Arch. Intern. med.* (Chicago), *113, 449.*

155 SCHAIE, K. W. (1966) – 'On the Relation of Colour and Personality'. *J. Project. Techn., 30, 512.*

156 SCHNECK, J. M. (1965) – 'Macropsie'. *Amer. J. Psychiat., 121,* 1123.

157 SCHOPLER, E. (1966) – 'Birth order and preference between visual and tactile receptors'. *Percept. Motor Skills, 22, 74.*

158 SCHUMANN, H.-J. Von (1955) – 'Phänomenologische und psychoanalytische Untersuchung der Homerischen Träume'. *Acta Psychother.* (Basel), *3, 205.*

159 SENDEN, M. von (1932) – *Space and Sight.* English transln. by Peter Heath (1960), Butler and Tanner Ltd, Frome and London.

160 SIEGRIST, A. (1917) – 'Gesellschaft der Schweizerischen Augenärtze'. *Klin. Mbl. Augenheilk., 58, 601.*

161 SINGER, C. (1928) – *From Magic to Science.* Benn, London, p. 232.

162 SLATER, E. (1963) – 'The Colour Imagery of Poets'. *Schweizer Arch. Neurol. Psychiat., 91, 303.*

163 SNYAKIN, P. G. (1965) – 'Relationship between optics and cutaneous perception of Light in man'. *Fed. Proc. Transl. Suppl., 24, 661.*

164 SNYDER, F. (1965) – 'Progress in the new biology of dreaming'. *Amer. J. Psychiat., 122, 370.*

165 SORSBY, A. (1930) – 'On the Nature of Milton's Blindness'. *Brit. J. Ophthal., 14, 339.*

166 SPROULE, B. M. (1963) – 'Colour-shift in memory for colours'. *Proc. II Scottish Symposium on Colour,* Edinburgh.

167 STEINBERG, D. D. (1966) – 'Light sensed through Receptors in the Skin'. *Amer. J. Psychol.*, *79*, 324.

168 STEVEN, D. M. (1963) – 'The Dermal Light Sense'. *Biol. Rev.*, *38*, 204.

169 STEVENS, D. and WOLFF, H. (1905) – 'The Relationship of Myopia to performance on a test of levelling-sharpening'. *Percept. Motor Skills*, *21*, 399.

170 STREBEL, J. (1933) – 'Prolegomena optica zum bildnerischen Kunstschaffen'. *Klin. Mbl. Augenheilk.*, *91*, 258.

171 SUINN, R. M. (1967) – 'Anxiety and Colour Dreaming'. *Ment. Hyg.*, *51*, 27.

172 TAYLOR, G. H. (1912) – 'The Colour Sense in relation to the emotions'. *Lancet*, *1*, 683.

173 TAYLOR, R. E. and EISENMAN, R. (1964) – 'Perception and Production of Complexity by creative art students'. *J. Psychol.*, *57*, 239.

174 TENNYSON, Hallam (1897) – *Alfred Lord Tennyson, a Memoir.* Macmillan, London.

175 *Time* (1958) – Obituary on G. Rouault. 29 Feb.

176 TORILLHON, I. M. (1958) – MD Thesis. Quoted in *Time* magazine 17 Feb.

177 TREVOR-ROPER, P. D. (1969) – 'The psychopathology of colour'. *Trans. Ophthal. Soc. UK*, *89*.

178 VALOIS, R. A. de; JACOBS, G. H. (1968) – 'Primate Colour Vision'. *Science*, *162*, 533.

179 VANDERPLAS, J. M. and GARVIN, E. A. (1959) – 'The Association value of Random Shapes'. *J. Exp. Psychol.*, *57*, 147.

180 VERNON, P. E. and STRAKER, A. (1943) – 'Distribution of Colour-blind Men in Great Britain'. *Nature*, *152*, 690.

181 VILLA ORTIZ, J. M. Jr. (1934) – 'El Rol de la Oftalmologia en la Cienca, el Arte y la Historia'. *Rev. Ophthal.* (S. Paulo), *3*, 203.

182 VILLEY, Pierre (1930) – *The World of the Blind.* Trans. by Alys Hallard. Duckworth, London.

183 VOLLARD, A. (1925) – *An Intimate Portrait.* Trans. by R. T. Weaver. Allen & Unwin, London. (USA 1928). p. 115.

184 WALLACE, Wm. (1888) – 'The Field of Vision'. MD Thesis, Univ. of Glasgow.

185 WARDROP, James (1826) – 'Case of a lady born blind, who received sight at an advanced age by the formation of an artificial pupil'. *Philos. Trans.*, *116*, 529.

186 WARE, James (1810) – 'Case of a young gentleman who recovered his sight when seven years of age after having been deprived of it by cataracts before he was a year old; with remarks'. *Philosoph. Trans.*, *91*, 382.

187 WATERHOUSE, E. K. (1941) – *Reynolds*. Kegan Paul, Trench, Trubner & Co. Ltd, London.

188 WEINSTEIN, P. (1958) – *Szemünk Világa*. Budapest.

189 WILENSKI, R. (1929) – *Dutch Art*. Faber and Gwyer, London.

190 WILMER, W. H. (1933) – 'The Blindness of Milton'. *Bull. Int. hist. med., 1*, 85.

191 WILSON, A. (1958) – 'A new theory of Perspective' (unpublished monograph).

192 WILSON, J. F. (1948) – 'Adjustments to Blindness'. *Brit. J. Psychol., 38*, 218.

193 WINNICOTT, Donald W. (1944) – 'Ocular Psychoneuroses'. *Trans. Ophthal. Soc. UK, 64*, 46.

194 YAKOLEV, P. I. (1963) – 'Telokinesis and handedness (an empirical generalisation)'. *Recent Advances Biol. Psychiat., 6*, 21.

195 YAZMAJIAN, R. V. (1968) – 'Dreams completely in colour'. *J. Amer. Psych. and Arts, 16*, 32.

196 YOUNG, F. A. (1967) – 'Myopia and Personality'. *Amer. J. Optom., 44*, 192.

List of Illustrations

Monochrome Plates

Medical Illustration at Westminster Hospital and the Institute of Ophthalmology.

14 Hypermetropic view. Photo Dr Peter Hansell and his Department of Medical Illustration at Westminster Hospital and the Institute of Ophthalmology.

15 Edward Gordon Craig: Projected design for Act II of Ibsen's *The Vikings*, 1903. Drawing. Bibliothèque Nationale, Paris.

16 Edgar Degas: *The Bath*, 1885. Pastel. Reproduced by kind permission of Mrs Charles Suydam Cutting, New York.

17 Edgar Degas: *Pregnant Woman, c.* 1896–1911. Bronze. The Joseph H. Hirshhorn Collection, New York.

18 Auguste Rodin: *The Age of Bronze*, 1875–77. Bronze. Tate Gallery, London.

19 Canaletto: *Greenwich Hospital from the north bank of the Thames, c.* 1748. Painting. National Maritime Museum, Greenwich.

20 A 'Claude Glass', widely used by artists in the late eighteenth century. Blackened glass in a velvet-lined box. Science Museum, London.

21 View in the Wye valley by an artist using a 'Claude Glass'. Aquatint. From W. Gilpin: *Observations on the River Wye*, 1782.

22 Rembrandt van Rijn: *Portrait of Saskia, c.* 1634. Painting. Staatliche Kunsthalle, Cassel.

23 Rembrandt van Rijn: *Self-portrait, c.* 1668. Painting. Wallraf-Richartz Museum, Cologne.

24 Titian (Tiziano Vecelli): *Sacred and Profane Love, c.* 1515–16. Painting. Borghese Gallery, Rome. Photo Mansell-Anderson.

25 Titian (Tiziano Vecelli): *The Flaying of Marsyas, c.* 1570. Painting. Archiepiscopal Castle, Kremsier.

26 El Greco (Domenicos Theotocopoulos): *Cardinal Fernando Nino de Guevara*, 1600. Painting. The Metropolitan Museum of Art, New York. Bequest of Mrs H. O. Havemeyer, 1929. The H. O. Havemeyer Collection.

27 El Greco (Domenicos Theotocopoulos): *Cardinal Fernando Nino de Guevara* photographed through an 'astigmatic' lens at 15°. From O. Ahlström: 'The Eyesight of some Renaissance Artists' in *Optical Scientific Instrument Maker*, 1955.

28 El Greco (Domenicos Theotocopoulos): *St Peter and St Paul, c.* 1592. Painting. Nationalmuseum, Stockholm.

29 El Greco (Domenicos Theotocopoulos): *St Peter and St Paul* photographed through an 'astigmatic' lens at 15°. From O. Ahlström, *op. cit.*

30 Hans Holbein the Younger: *Henry VIII*, 1539–40. Painting. Galleria Nazionale, Rome. Photo Gabinetto Fotografico Nazionale, Rome.

31 Hans Holbein the Younger: *Henry VIII* photographed through an 'astigmatic' lens at 90°. From O. Ahlström, *op. cit.*

53 Piero della Francesca: *Federigo da Montefeltro, Duke of Urbino,* *c.* 1465. Painting. Uffizi, Florence. Photo Mansell-Anderson.

54 Diego Rodriguez de Silva Velazquez: *Jacob receiving the blood-stained coat of Joseph,* 1630. Painting. Escorial, Madrid. Photo Mas.

55 Diego Rodriguez de Silva Velazquez: *Jacob receiving the blood-stained coat of Joseph* (reversed). Photo Mas.

56 Edvard Munch: T. No. 2138, 1930. Drawing. Munch-Museet, Oslo.

57 Edvard Munch: T. No. 2152, 1930. Drawing. Munch-Museet, Oslo.

58 Edvard Munch: T. No. 2150, 1930. Watercolour. Munch-Museet, Oslo.

59 L. Matéfy: Drawing made under the influence of LSD 25. Triangle, the Sandoz Journal of Medical Science.

60 L. Matéfy: Drawing made under the influence of LSD 25. Triangle, the Sandoz Journal of Medical Science.

61 L. Matéfy: Drawing made under the influence of LSD 25. Triangle, the Sandoz Journal of Medical Science.

62 St Hildegard with Volmer her secretary. From *Scivias,* 1141–51, f. 1. Hessische Landesbibliothek, Wiesbaden.

63 Egyptian stele showing singer of Amon playing the harp before Horus, dynasty XIX (1314–1197 BC). Painted wood. Louvre, Paris. Photo Giraudon.

64 Roman Mithraic relief with Helios and Selene, early third century. Stone. Antiquario Comunale, Rome.

65 Oedipus putting out his eyes. Italian miniature from a 1475 edition of Seneca's *Tragedies.* Biblioteca Marciana, Venice.

66 Head of Siva from Por Loboek, Siemreap, mid-eleventh century. Gilded bronze. Repository of Angkor Conservancy, Siemreap.

67 Jacopo Tintoretto: *Susanna and the Elders, c.* 1560. Painting. Kunsthistorisches Museum, Vienna.

68, Three stages in the mastery of painting by a congenitally 'near-
69, blind' boy who had gross peripheral field restriction. From V.
70 Löwenfeld: 'Psycho-Aesthetic Implications of the Art of the Blind' in *The Journal of Aesthetics and Art Criticism,* Sept. 1951.

71, Three stages in the mastery of sculpture by a congenitally blind
72, boy. From V. Löwenfeld: 'Psycho-Aesthetic Implications of the
73 Art of the Blind' in *The Journal of Aesthetics and Art Criticism,* September 1951.

74– Sculptures by blind people. From G. Révész: *Psychology and Art*
76 *of the Blind,* 1950. (Published by Longmans, London.)

77 Pieter Brueghel: *Parable of the Blind,* 1568. Painting. Museo di Capodimonte, Naples. Photo Soprintendenza alle Gallerie, Naples.

78 Attributed to Rodrigo de Osuna (active 1476–84): *St Lucy.* Painting. Museo Provincial, Valencia. Photo Mas.

INDEX

Numbers in italics refer to black-and-white illustrations, roman numerals to colour plates.

Coates, W. H., 154, 155

Coleridge, Samuel Taylor, 67

colour: associations with music, 68f.; blindness, 53, 75–86; blindness in animals, 164; blindness in industry, 82–3; blindness in painters, 83f., 167f.; blindness, racial distribution, 75, 82, 92; blindness in writers, 83; capacity for distortion, 53–64, VI, VII, VIII; in birds, 54f.; in fish, 54; in lower mammals, 55; in molluscs, arthropods and insects, 55, 164; in dreams, 72; effect on human behaviour, 69f.; environmental, 69–70; linguistic distortions, 63; preferences – in apes, 62; in children, 65; in the deaf, 66; in myopes and hypermetropes, 35; in primitive races, 63; in schizophrenics, 66; secondary distortions, 91; symbolic significance of, 65, 67, 72f.; temperamental response to, 64f.; therapy, 71; use by birds in sexual display, 55–62; vision, 53f.

Constable, John, 84f., XI

convex mirror used by painters, 51, 164

Copeau, Jacques, 34

Corot, Jean Baptiste Camille, 85, 93

correction of sight, 11, 38, 49, 71

Correggio, 95n., *41*

Craig, E. Gordon, 34, 164, *15*

Cranach, Lucas (the Elder), 49, *34*

Cross, Mr (Vicar of Chew Magna, Somerset), 52

DALTON, John, 82

Daumier, Honoré, 37n.

Davidson and Hemmendiger colour rule, 168

Davie, 171

Degas, Edgar, 33, *16, 17*

Delius, Frederick, 157

Democritus, 149, 165

Demodocus, 157

Derain, André, 34

dermo–optical perception, 150f., 152, 171

Diderot, Denis, 153n.

disparity of retinal images *see* aniseikonia, squint

Doesschate, G. Ten, 71

Donnet, L., 64

Dorn, 166

Dou, Gerald, 164

Douglas, Norman, 63

dreams, 72f.

Droste-Hülshoff, Annette von, 29

drugs, 92, 131; effect on perception, 132f., 169

Dufy, Raoul, 34

Dürer, Albrecht, 95f., 102, *44, 45, 46, 47, 48, 49*

dyslexia, 168

ELONGATION of retinal image *see* astigmatism

Euclid, 169

Evans, Merlyn, 134

Evil Eye, 148, 169

Ewart, A. G., 170

eye, optical structure, 11f., 118f.; ageing, *see* presbyopia, glaucoma; damage, *see* cataract, retinal detachment, glaucoma, pituitary tumour; divergence or convergence in perception, *see* aniseikonia, squint; 'eye dominance', 104, 167f.; in painters, 107; movements, 94f., 106f., 118f.; sexual connotations, *see* scotophilia, Evil Eye; strain, 38

FAITHORNE, William, 5

Farington, Joseph, 85

Fisher, C. M., 160f.

Francesca, Piero della, 37n., *53*

Freud, Sigmund, 72, 145, 146

Fry, Sara Margery, 151

GAINSBOROUGH, Thomas, 50n., *37*

Galen, 92

Galton, Francis, 82

Gibbon, Edward, 31, 171

glaucoma, 119